EASY READING
SHAKESPEARE
VOLUME TWO

By the same author:

Easy Reading Shakespeare Volume One: The Bard in Bite-Size Verse, The Book Guild, 2005

Kenneth Grahame's The Wind in the Willows in Bite-Size Verse, The Book Guild, 2005

EASY READING SHAKESPEARE

VOLUME TWO

The Bard in Bite-Size Verse

Richard Cuddington

Book Guild Publishing

Sussex, England

First published in Great Britain in 2006 by
The Book Guild Ltd
25 High Street
Lewes, East Sussex
BN7 2LU

Typesetting in Times by
Keyboard Services, Luton, Bedfordshire

Printed in Great Britain by
Antony Rowe Ltd, Chippenham, Wiltshire

A catalogue record for this book is available from
The British Library

ISBN 1 84624 000 X

For Beatrice and Ernest

CONTENTS

She had an awful temper

THE TAMING OF THE SHREW

Baptista lived in Padua
With both his daughters fair.
It was a lovely little town
And he liked living there.

Life should have been so easy –
But sometimes he felt harried
Because his darling daughters
Weren't settled down and married.

The youngest, called Bianca,
Had many suitors bid
For her hand – she really was
A lovely-looking kid.

The older sister, Katharine
Was no such lovely dish,
She was a totally different
Kettleful of fish.

She had an awful temper
As everybody knew,
And she would never do a thing
That she was told to do.

Really quite unruly,
A problem to her dad,
He'd given up all hope that she
Would find herself a lad.

Because the long and short of it,
The whole truth – what the heck!
Was simply this – that Katharine was
A right pain in the neck.

And this was why she'd earned the name
That far and wide all knew,
Why she was known in Padua
As Katharine, the shrew.

Baptista now had made it plain
Bianca couldn't wed –
'No, not before your sister,'
Is what he'd always said.

So all Bianca's suitors
Got told to sling their hook.
They had to satisfy themselves
With just a measly look.

But then one day a bold, brave guy,
Petruchio by name,
Came bowling into Padua –
Wife-seeking was his game.

Of Katharine's reputation
He'd been told – and to beware.
His response – 'I'm not too bothered;
I really couldn't care.'

He knew that she was rich and fair –
That was the crucial thing –
And he was quite determined
To give the girl a ring.

He was a cunning devil,
He planned a devious game,
For he was sure that he knew how
To very quickly tame

The wilful, wild, unruly girl
And teach her to behave.
He was without a trace of doubt
A very clever knave.

His normal character was calm,
And humorous and funny,
But he could cover this to win
A servile wife with money.

His plan was once he'd won her,
To act in such a way
To make the crazy Katharine
Experience the dismay

That she so often handed out.
He'd show his temper more
Than Katharine could – she wouldn't like
The moods he had in store.

But by these means he felt quite sure
That he could make her feel
Respect and love towards him,
And bring this shrew to heel.

He went to see Baptista,
'Look here,' he calmly said,
'I fancy your girl, Katharine.
I'd like for us to wed.'

Petruchio pretended that
He thought her meek and mild,
He didn't let Baptista know
He knew that she was wild.

Baptista though could clearly see
Petruchio was keen,
And being an honest fellow
He decently came clean.

He said, 'I'd like to see her wed –
Of this there is no doubt –
But I don't think you understand
What Katharine's all about.'

He went to see Baptista

And he was just about to tell
Petruchio the truth
When Katharine's music teacher rushed
Straight in and cried out ''Strewth!'

The girl had hit him with her lute,
And just for merely saying
He wasn't happy with the way
That Katharine had been playing.

Petruchio was not deterred
By what he clearly saw.
He said, 'She's sounds a brassy lass;
I love her even more.

'So tell me, good Baptista,
What do I have to do
To gain your kind permission
To go to her and woo?

'You know I am not short of cash –
My father, who's now dead,
Has left me quite a fortune,'
He up and boldly said.

'So can you now inform me
What will her dowry be.
If I take Katharine off your hands
What will you give to me?'

Baptista found his manner blunt,
But he had cash and lands
And was prepared to give some up
To get her off his hands.

'I'll give you twenty thousand crowns
And land when I should die.
I cannot offer more than that,'
He said with a deep sigh.

Petruchio was very pleased;
A deal was quickly done.
Petruchio would get the cash,
Baptista a new son.

And Katharine would be a bride –
Baptista went to tell
His daughter who, he felt quite sure,
Would scream and storm and yell.

Now Petruchio began to mould
The outline of his plan.
He determined that he'd play
The even-tempered man.

If she had a go at him
Or seemed as cold as ice,
He would pretend he found it all
Attractive, sweet and nice.

Or if she wouldn't speak to him,
He wouldn't take offence.
Instead he'd praise her loudly
For her marvellous eloquence.

And if she told him to be gone
He'd utter not a squeak;
He'd thank her just as if she'd asked
For him to stay a week.

When Katharine came into the room,
Petruchio said, 'Good Kate...'
But she replied, 'Don't call me that,
For it's a name I hate.

'My proper name is Katharine.'
Her wrath was clear to see.
'And that's how I must be addressed
If you would speak to me.'

'You lie,' Petruchio boldly said.
(A funny way to woo!)
'They call you bonny, pretty Kate –
And sometimes "Kate, the shrew".

'Because I've heard your mildness
Is praised in every town
I've come right here to woo you.'
Kate's face took on a frown.

They were left there on their own
And Katharine made it clear
Why men had been convinced that she
Was someone they should fear.

And while she raved and carried on
Like you have never heard,
He remained relaxed and cool
And praised her every word.

Then finally he said, 'Sweet Kate,
Don't make all this to-do,
For I am quite determined
That I will marry you.'

Just then Baptista came right back
And sly Petruchio said,
'Your daughter Kate has now agreed
The two of us can wed.'

But Kate denied this strongly,
Using quite the basest slang.
She said, 'I will not marry you;
I'd rather see you hang.'

She cried, 'How could I father, wed
A frightful brute like this?'
Petruchio lied, 'When on our own
We both exchanged a kiss.'

He quite convinced Baptista
That Kate's love for him was true.
He said, 'She's merely putting on
This angry show for you.

'So give me now your hand, fair Kate.
To Venice I will go
To buy you fancy garments –
I'll be back before you know.

'We'll marry Sunday morning
So kiss me, Kate – farewell.
Baptista, please prepare a feast
And ring the wedding bell.'

When Sunday came one thing did not –
That was Petruchio.
Katharine cried, 'Why's he not here?'
They all said, 'We don't know.'

'So give me now your hand, fair Kate'

Katharine wept from sheer vexation,
Called him 'worthless cur'.
Had his proposal been a joke?
Just making fun of her?

But then he suddenly appeared –
He burst into the room.
But he was not attired to be
A smart and proper groom.

His clothes were worn and dirty
And he seemed to bear the stamp
Of common, hard-up working men –
He looked just like a tramp.

His retinue and servants –
Well, they also looked a mess;
And there was not the slightest sign
Of Katharine's promised dress.

They tried to get Petruchio
To change his scruffy gear,
But he just said to Katharine,
'It's me you wed, my dear.

'It's not my clothes you're marrying,
So don't make all this fuss.
Let's get ourselves into the church –
There's no more to discuss.'

He looked just like a tramp

The party headed off to church
On this the wedding day,
Petruchio just carrying on
In his eccentric way.

And when the priest stepped up and said,
'Is Kate to be your wife?'
Petruchio swore so loudly that
Astonishment was rife.

Everyone was quite amazed –
It showed in every look.
The priest was so astounded that
He dropped his big, black book.

And as he stooped to pick it up,
Quite clearly in a huff,
Petruchio leant forward
And he gave the priest a cuff.

This sent the poor man reeling,
And his book fell on the floor.
Recovering the sacred tome,
The priest began once more.

And through it all Petruchio stamped
Or swore and wore a sneer,
While Katharine stood there trembling –
The poor girl shook with fear.

And he gave the priest a cuff

Once he and Kate were married,
He said, 'Kiss me now, you're mine.'
Then in a raucous voice he yelled,
'Bring me a flask of wine.'

He deeply drank, then toasted
Everybody in the place;
And then he threw a glass of wine
Right in the sexton's face.

He claimed the sexton's beard
Was lank and grew too thin.
It was so drab and mangy
It showed his pasty skin.

He said this was his reason
For acting like a cad,
But he was just pretending
To be completely mad.

'Twas part and parcel of his scheme
(Though others had no clue)
To tame his wild, unruly wife,
Young Katharine, the shrew.

Baptista had prepared a feast –
It was a sumptuous spread.
Petruchio ignored it all –
'We're going home,' he said.

Baptista remonstrated;
The bride was angry too.
Petruchio would not be swayed
From what he wished to do.

'We're going now,' he loudly said.
'My wife does what I say.'
And with those words he angrily
Dragged Katharine away.

He placed her on a scraggy horse,
In such a sorry state
The poor bedraggled creature
Could hardly take her weight.

He placed her on a scraggy horse

As they travelled on their way
The only sound she heard
Were ravings from her husband,
And she quaked at every word.

She was delighted to alight
Once they had reached his house,
But there was now much worse in store
For Katharine from her spouse.

For he'd made up his mind she'd not
Get anything to eat,
Or even get the chance to rest
Or ease her weary feet.

For when the servants laid a meal
With meat and veg and fish,
Petruchio took pains to find
Some fault with every dish.

He threw the food onto the floor.
He cried, 'Not good enough!
This will not do for you, my love.
You shall not eat this stuff.'

So Katharine went to bed at last,
Hungry and tired out.
But when Petruchio saw their bed
He raised his voice to shout.

'This bed is badly made,' he cried.
'The pillows are too hard.'
And then he threw the linen sheets
Straight out into the yard.

Katharine was badly shaken,
'I'll sleep in this chair,' she said.
Petruchio spent half the night
Just slagging off the bed.

He yelled about the servants
So she didn't get much sleep,
And by the time the morning came
Poor Kate was fit to weep.

And then when breakfast was served up
Petruchio was the same:
Pretending to act kindly
He played the self-same game.

He said the food was rubbish
And to her despair once more
He threw each tasty morsel
Onto the parlour floor.

Petruchio at last went out
And stuck up, haughty Kate
Was forced to beg the servants
For just *something* on a plate.

She pleaded with the servants,
'Some food – oh, I entreat,
For I am truly famished.
Bring me something here to eat.'

But they said they didn't dare –
Their master would be sore.
She cried, 'But beggars get more food,
Who knock at father's door.

'And here am I – I'm almost starved,
As tired as one can be.
My husband claims he only acts
Just out of love for me.'

And then Petruchio returned.
He said, 'Look, I've brought you
Some meat that I have just prepared –
I've made a tasty stew.'

It was a tiny portion
But it seemed a mighty treat,
Katharine was delighted that
She had some food to eat.

Before she'd finished eating it
He took the food away.
He said, 'I can't allow my wife
To over-eat today.

'Besides I've called the tailor
Who's made some lovely things:
Silken coats and caps and ruffs,
And here – some golden rings.

'And when you've tried them on, my dear,'
Exclaimed her loving spouse,
'We'll go and make a visit
To your father's charming house.'

But this of course was all a sham.
Petruchio once more
Was playing with his hungry wife
Whom he *would* tame for sure.

For when she tried the garments on
He cried, 'Great heavens above!
You can't go out in clothes like that –
It wouldn't do, my love.'

He said, 'You can't call that a sleeve...
The thing's a total mess –
And I must say quite truthfully
That is an awful dress.'

He drove the tailor from the room.
(The man was duly paid –
Petruchio made sure he knew
He thought the dress well made).

This was all a further step
Along the road he'd planned.
He told it to the tailor
So he would understand.

Then to Kate he turned and said,
'We'll go and see your dad
Dressed in these scruffy clothes instead –
They're really not that bad.'

Katharine didn't argue,
For she had given up.
She thought, 'At least at father's house,
I'll get a chance to sup.'

They left to see Baptista –
Kate had lost her wild ambition;
Her crazy spouse had beaten her
Into complete submission.

They met a man whilst travelling
Along a tree-lined glade.
Petruchio addressed him:
'Good morrow, gentle maid.'

Yes – he called him 'gentle maid'.
Was this some kind of joke?
Why was he playing games like this
With this white-haired old bloke?

'*Good morrow, gentle maid*'

Well, he wished to ascertain
If he had tamed poor Kate,
If he had made her lose for good
Her every wilful trait.

Her spirit now was vanquished,
She had no will to fight –
She acted in a way to show
That all he said was right.

So she addressed the ancient man:
'It is so nice to meet
A young and budding virgin,
So fair and fresh and sweet.'

The moment that she spoke these words
Petruchio up and said,
'Why how now, Kate – have you gone mad?
Have you quite lost your head?

'This is a wrinkled, withered man,
No maiden as you say.'
Then Kate replied, 'The sun's bright light
Has dazzled me today.

'I now can see that you're a man,'
She said with heavy sighs.
'Pray pardon me for my mistake –
The sun got in my eyes.'

So we can see, through loss of sleep
And lack of a good meal,
And by her husband's craziness,
How Kate was brought to heel.

'Good sire,' Petruchio then said,
'Where do you go today?
We'd love it if you'd come with us,
And help us on our way.'

The old man said, 'I'm travelling
To Padua – to my son.
For he is getting married,
For he has lately won

The hand of fair Bianca –
Baptista's girl, you know.
His first name is Lucentio,
And he is now her beau.'

The old man was Vincentio –
Petruchio knew his name –
And as their destination
Was going to be the same

They travelled on together
To old Baptista's house
Where young Lucentio then took
Bianca for his spouse.

Another pair had also wed –
Hortensio was the groom;
So all these happy people
Were gathered in one room.

The grooms were talking later,
And then they made a joke
About Petruchio's sour wife,
And this is how they spoke:

They said, 'How can he bear her?
She's such a shrewish wife.
Her wilful disposition
Cuts the air just like a knife.'

They said, 'We're very lucky
To have wives who are so nice;
They're calm and easy-going
And free of any vice.

'Petruchio has his work cut out,
A handful there – not 'arf.'
They clapped each other on the back
And had a hearty laugh.

But after they had dined and when
The ladies all withdrew,
They started poking fun again,
They said, 'Your Kate's a shrew.'

Petruchio denied it.
He said, 'Let's set a test.
We'll have a little wager;
We'll have a little jest.

'We'll see which wife turns out the most
Obedient of all –
We'll see which one comes straight away
When each one gives a call.'

The two new grooms agreed at once.
They saw no cause to fret;
They were convinced that they would win
So they proposed a bet.

'We'll wager twenty crowns,' they said.
Petruchio answered, 'No!
If we are going to have a bet
Let's bet some proper dough.

'Make it a hundred crowns,' he said.
So that's what they agreed.
Lucentio sent a servant then
To Bianca, with all speed.

'Tell her to come here right away.'
Her answer struck him dumb,
The servant said, 'My mistress claims
She's too tied up to come.'

At once Hortensio spoke up.
He said, 'Entreat my wife.'
Petruchio said, 'I've never heard
Such rubbish in my life.'

The servant scurried off and then
Came back and said, 'Good sir,
She says you must be joking
And bids you come to her.'

So finally Petruchio spoke.
'Go to my wife,' says he.
'Command her presence here at once –
Tell her to come to me.'

The company all gasped aloud –
They were convinced as one
That fiery, headstrong Katharine
Would never ever come.

But lo! Within an instant
Katharine stood before her Lord.
Astounded was the company –
It made them all applaud.

'What do you wish?' Kate meekly asked.
'What service can I do?
Anything you want, my Lord,
That I will do for you.'

'What do you wish?' Kate meekly asked

'The wives of these good gentlemen,
Go fetch them,' he replied.
'Their wilful disobedience
I really can't abide.'

So Katharine went to get them –
And shortly brought them back.
Petruchio said, 'Now you shall see
What your two women lack.'

And with the ladies standing there
Petruchio said, 'Now Kate,
You teach them good behaviour
And how to treat their mate.'

So Katharine told the sullen girls,
Quite of her own accord,
How they should treat their husbands,
And their duty to their Lord.

Thus it was clear to one and all,
Petruchio, by skill,
Had now entirely taught his wife
To gladly do his will.

Katharine became the fairest wife
That all in Padua knew,
No longer disobedient –
And no longer called 'the shrew'!

So every day he'd get complaints

MEASURE FOR MEASURE

Laws are there to be obeyed –
I think that's fair enough.
But sometimes folk will take no heed
Of all that legal stuff.

Thus it was in old Vienna,
For there they had a law
That all the city's residents
Chose simply to ignore.

It stated that you couldn't live
With someone not your wife;
And if this law was broken
You stood to lose your life.

But the Duke who should enforce
The laws the State had made
Took very little trouble
To ensure they were obeyed.

So every day he'd get complaints
By parents who were mad
Because their daughters chose to live
With men they thought were bad.

Marriage grew uncommon –
A sad state of affairs.
No wonder parents were stressed out
With all these many cares.

The Duke saw something must be done
But he was scared to act
Because the people loved him –
He knew this for a fact.

So if he changed completely,
And now enforced the law,
He feared that his good subjects
Would not love him anymore.

So he decided that he'd leave
Vienna for a while,
Putting someone else in charge
Who had a different style.

Then the law could be applied,
And he'd not get the blame.
He chose a friend to take the helm,
One Angelo by name.

Now Angelo was one they thought
Had led a blameless life;
He was the man to make quite sure
That young men took a wife.

His reputation spotless,
He really was a saint,
He was the man without a doubt
To sort out a complaint.

Even the Duke's chief counsellor,
Lord Escalus by name,
Declared at once that Angelo
Would stop the young folk's game.

The Duke said, 'I'll to Poland.'
But he didn't really go;
He dressed up as a friar
So that no-one there would know

That he was in Vienna still.
His reason was, you see,
To keep an eye on Angelo,
To find out if he'd be

A better man at running things.
He thought, 'Will Angelo
Get things done more efficiently?
I really have to know.'

Now just when Angelo took charge
A man called Claudio
Seduced a fair young lady –
He claimed he loved her so.

He dressed up as a friar

Said Angelo immediately,
'Since this has now arisen
I know the course we must pursue:
Fling Claudio into prison.

'And he must pay the penalty
For this great wrong,' he said,
'And so I sentence him to lose
His most unworthy head.'

Lord Escalus was very shocked
And tried to intervene.
He said, 'Beheading Claudio
Will seem extremely mean.

'Besides, his dad's a decent chap;
For *his* sake, please forgive.
For mercy's sake, show some restraint
And let the young man live.'

But Angelo would not be moved.
He said, 'One thing's for sure –
If we release him, then we make
A scarecrow of the law.

'We set the law to frighten
All gloating birds of prey,
But then we let them perch on it
And don't chase them away.

'So it becomes a comfy perch,
And causes no-one terror...
Now if we let this happen
It will be a major error.

'This is my way of thinking,
And this, my reason why,
The prisoner can't be released
And why he has to die.'

Claudio's old friend, Lucio,
Went to him in the jail;
He said, 'You're in big trouble –
They won't allow you bail.

'In fact, the word out on the street
Is that you're dead for sure.
Angelo has made it clear
He will uphold the law.

'The Duke would have excused you,'
Good Lucio quietly said,
'But this self-righteous idiot
Simply wants you dead.'

Claudio said, 'I've got one hope:
Go to my sister, pray.
She enters Saint Clare's nunnery
To take the veil today.

'Go tell my sister Isabel
About the mess I'm in.
Tell her – she is my only hope –
She is my closest kin.

'Ask her to go to Angelo
And beg him pardon me;
I'm sure her fluent discourse and
Her prayers can make him see

'That I do not deserve to die.
Tell her to beg the Lord
To grant me a reprieve – and say
He's going overboard.'

The convent had received her,
She was speaking to a nun,
Learning all the many rules
Of what she'd now begun,

When suddenly they heard a voice.
'Who's that?' cried Isabel.
'Please go and check,' the nun replied,
'And then return and tell.

'For I can't speak to any man,
I can't return his hail;
It is forbidden totally,
Once you're beneath the veil.

'And hark! – I hear him call again.
Please go to him, I pray,
And ask him why he breaks the peace
Of convent life today.'

Isabel obeyed the nun.
She went to Lucio
And said, 'Why are you yelling out?
The nuns all want to know.'

Then Lucio said, 'Fair virgin, maid –
For so you seem to be –
I seek a novice, Isabel,
To give some help to me.

'Unhappy Claudio sent me –
He's in a sorry state.
Only his loving sister can
Now save him from his fate.'

'*Unhappy* – why?' asked Isabel.
'I am the one you seek.
What's happened to my brother
Since I spoke to him last week?'

Lucio said, 'He's been locked up,
He has seduced a maid,
And sends me here to ask if you
Will come now to his aid.'

'It's Juliet,' said Isabel.
'She is a friend of mine.
But surely if he marries her
Then all will be just fine.'

Lucio replied, 'Of course,
That would be common sense.
But Angelo insists he die,
Just for this small offence.

'Why, Claudio would marry her
At once – for this I know –
But Angelo will not agree
And lets his hatred grow.

'So Claudio's fervent hope is that
You will now go and see
This Angelo – and with your prayers
You'll set your brother free.'

'Will Angelo,' said Isabel,
Pay any heed to me?
Why in the world would he give ear
To my unworthy plea?'

Said Lucio, 'There is a chance –
When maidens weep and kneel
It really is amazing
What tears can make men feel.

'It makes them feel important –
Even a useless clod
Believes he's something special
And thinks that he's a god.

'So go to good Lord Angelo
And do the best you can,
And though he acts as if he's God,
Remember he's a man.'

Isabel ran to the court
And said to Angelo,
'I am a humble sister
Borne down with grief and woe.'

He answered her in haughty tones,
(In truth he thought her cute)
'So tell me then, young lady,
What's the nature of your suit?'

She pleaded for her brother's life
In the most moving way.
Angelo listened patiently
To all she had to say.

When she had finished he declared,
By way of a reply,
'Nothing can save your brother,
I'm afraid that he must die.'

She knelt to him for mercy –
He gave it to her straight:
'No power on Earth can save him,
He's sentenced – it's too late.'

She cried, 'If my poor brother
Were not himself, but you,
I feel I know for certain
Exactly what he'd do.

'A sister's plea would move him,
He wouldn't be so stern,
And this unhappy sentence,
I know he'd overturn.'

'You must accept,' said Angelo,
'What now he's got in store.
It is the proper sentence;
It is Vienna's law.

'Were he my dearest kinsman,
My brother or my son,
The law would have to run its course
For the crime that he has done.

'And for this reason, I'm afraid
Your brother dies tomorrow.'
'Oh spare him,' Isabel cried out,
Borne down with dreadful sorrow.

'No-one else has paid this price
For doing what he's done.
If you sentence him to death
He'll be the only one.

'Knock on the doorway of your heart
And ask the reason why
You think it so imperative
My dear brother die.'

She looked at him with big brown eyes,
Her face was drawn and ashen;
Her beauty made him start to feel
An overpowering passion.

His mind was now in conflict –
He wondered what to do.
Then Isabel cried desperately,
'Can bribes amend your view?'

'What's that you say?' he sternly asked.
'How could you even dare?'
'Oh, not with treasure, Lord,' she said,
'But with a fervent prayer.'

'Come tomorrow,' he replied,
'I'll hear no more today.'
She left him grateful that she'd gained
A day's reprieve this way.

Once she had gone, sly Angelo
Reflected very much.
'Perhaps I am in love,' he thought.
'I hunger for her touch.

'I've never felt this way before –
I've always been above
Such feelings – for I've always laughed
When others are in love.'

That night he could not sleep at all;
Her image filled his head.
I think we all can guess just where
His naughty thoughts now led.

He struggled to resist them,
But he was doomed to fail...
He'd tell her of a way to get
Her brother out of jail.

Yes – he who'd hardly listened
To her desperate diatribe
In which she'd offered openly
Her pious, prayerful bribe

Would turn to his advantage now
Her current state of strife:
He would seduce her in exchange
For her dear brother's life.

⚜

So when she came next morning –
He said, 'Just yield to me,
Give up your virgin honour
And I'll set Claudio free.

'For I adore you, Isabel;
My feelings are sincere.'
She said, 'That's how my brother felt;
He held his Juliet dear.

'And for this he is to die –
Surely that's not right.'
'Oh, he shall live, if you,' he said,
'Will come to me tonight.'

Isabel was horrified
That he proposed this pact –
The same as Claudio had done:
It was the self-same act.

He said, 'Just yield to me'

'Is this to test my virtue?'
She said in great dismay.
'This *has* to be the reason
You speak to me this way.'

He replied, 'It is no test,
I mean just what I speak.
By this pact we each can gain
The object that we seek.'

Isabel was furious
At all that he unfurled.
She cried with great emotion,
'I shall tell the whole wide world,

'Just what kind of man you are.'
He said, 'You try that game,
And no-one will believe you –
Remember my good name.

'I'm well-known for my pious ways,
So do not waste your time.
Do what I want or Claudio
Will perish for his crime.

'Take care before you answer,
Come along tomorrow;
Agree to my suggestion
And put an end to sorrow.'

Isabel left Angelo
Feeling much maligned;
She went to see poor Claudio
In the place he was confined.

Arriving at the jail she went
Straight to her brother's cell;
She found a pious, friendly friar
Was visiting as well.

This was, in fact, the noble Duke
Whom no-one recognised,
For he was cleverly attired –
Quite artfully disguised.

He'd spoken to fair Juliet,
Depressed by what she'd done;
She'd claimed, 'It isn't Claudio's fault,
I am the guilty one.'

And then he'd come to Claudio
Who also was contrite.
The Duke was much encouraged for
They'd both learnt wrong from right.

When Isabel walked in, she gave
Poor Claudio a kiss.
The startled friar looked up and said,
'Who in the world is this?'

She said, 'I've come to speak a word
With my poor brother there.
Please leave us on our own awhile;
He'll profit from my care.'

The gentle friar left the cell
But he was keen to hear
The talk that passed between them,
So stood outside, quite near.

He heard young Claudio enquire,
Once he had closed the door,
'Tell me, good sister – what's the news?
Please tell me what's the score.'

Isabel endeavoured to
Be calm, and took a breath,
Then said, 'Dear brother, I'm afraid
You must prepare for death.'

'Oh, is there nothing to be done?
Is there no hope?' he said.
'You must accept,' she answered him,
'That you're as good as dead.

'For though there is a certain way
That I could rescue you,
I'd have to carry out an act
You'd not want me to do.

'For Angelo has promised,
If I sleep with him,' she said,
'He'll spare you – but the price I pay
Is I must share his bed.

'I would gladly give my life
To save you, brother dear,
But thus to lose my virtue
Would be too much, I fear.'

Claudio listened silently,
Then with a desperate cry
He said, 'Sweet sister, save me,
For I don't want to die.

'The deed that Angelo demands
Is not so much to give,
For it is one that will ensure
I have a chance to live.

'Nature will forgive you,
For I have heard folk say
A sin becomes a virtue
When committed in this way.

'Let me live, dear sister,
For you are now empowered
To save me – and it only means
That you will be deflowered.'

'Hear me out,' then Claudio cried...

She called him 'Faithless coward! Wretch!'
Said she despised his name
For wanting to preserve his life
By his poor sister's shame.

'If you had twenty heads to lose
On twenty blocks,' she said,
'They should be used, to save me from
This Angelo's foul bed.'

'Hear me out,' then Claudio cried...
Before he could say more
The Duke appeared in friar's garb
And peered around the door.

He said, 'I have heard everything,
And I say to both of you
That Angelo is not corrupt –
I can't believe it's true.

'It was a test for Isabel,
That's why he's done this act.
He'll be relieved when he finds out
Your honour is intact –

'So pleased that you denied him,
That you passed his little test.
Don't fret about it any more –
It's not a real request.

'But as for you, young Claudio,
There is no hope I fear,
All you can do is pray because
I feel your death draws near.'

Claudio then repented –
Ashamed for being weak,
He turned to face his sister:
'Please listen while I speak.

'Forgive me for my weakness,
Please try to pardon me;
I am so tired of life that death
Can come and set me free.'

Claudio was quite overwhelmed;
His sister then forgave –
She knew it was the fear of death
That made him play the knave.

She left then with the Duke, who said,
'The hand that made you fair
Was also one that made you good,
Of this I'm now aware.'

'Oh, dear!' she cried. 'If when he left
The Duke could have conceived
What Angelo would prove to be,
How he would be deceived,

'He'd not have left Vienna
In such untrue hands as these,
He'd not have let this Angelo
Become a foul disease.

'And if some day the Duke returns
I'll tell him all I know;
I'll tell him of my brother's death
And of vile Angelo.'

Little did she know that as
She made this stern rebuke,
The man to whom she now addressed
Her comments was the Duke.

The Duke replied that Angelo
Would say she told a lie,
Then said, 'I think I can make sure
That Claudio doesn't die.

'If you will do all that I say,
If you will just be strong,
I think that I can show a way
To right this dreadful wrong.'

Isabel replied that she
Would trust the holy friar,
For after all a man of God
Would scarcely be a liar.

The Duke then told her of his plan.
He asked, 'Now have you heard
Of Mariana, lone and sweet,
And what to her occurred?'

'I've heard about this lady,'
Fair Isabel replied.
'Well, sad to say,' the friar said,
'Her poor brother died.

'This Mariana is the wife
Of our Lord Angelo.'
'He's married then!' she cried, aghast.
'Well, that I didn't know.'

'Oh yes, he's good and married
But he now disowns his wife.
Her brother was at sea when thus
He sadly lost his life.

'He had his sister's dowry
To give to Angelo,
The ship went down and it was lost –
A really bitter blow.

'Though married then Lord Angelo
Disowned his faithful spouse;
He made up tales about her
And banned her from his house.

'I found this out just recently –
So this is what we'll do:
Tell Angelo that you agree
To what he's put to you.

'Say you will go at midnight,
And he must free your brother.
But Isabel, you will not go,
For we will send another.

'Mariana will be sent –
There is no sin in this,
For they're a married couple
So nought can be amiss.

'Mariana will agree
For I have been to her
To give her consolation –
I know that she'll concur.'

So Isabel to Angelo,
Returned and said, 'All right!
I'll do the very thing you ask
And come to you tonight.'

'And in return,' the Lord replied,
'I'll pardon Claudio.
So we have reached agreement –
But this you need to know:

'This key will gain admittance
To my palace here tonight.
Enter by the vine-yard gate
And keep well out of sight.'

So they agreed the meeting;
She left without a word,
Then went to meet the friar
To tell what had occurred.

He was at Mariana's.
She, delighted with the plan,
Was quite convinced it would unite
Her once more with her man.

Her face all veiled in shadows
And hidden from his sight,
Lord Angelo would never know
Who was his love that night.

So Mariana made her way
To see him as arranged.
She went disguised as Isabel –
Their roles had been exchanged.

Once she had gone to Angelo
The Duke, still dressed as friar,
Went to the prison, for he thought
Lord Angelo a liar.

It was very lucky that
He did so choose to go,
For word had just arrived, right then,
From evil Angelo.

The order was the very thing
That Isabel had dreaded.
It said that Claudio that night
Must swiftly be beheaded.

The document went on to say
That Claudio's severed head
Be brought to Angelo forthwith,
While he was still in bed.

What a devious, evil man
To trick poor Isabel!
The Duke on hearing this made haste
To check on Claudio's cell.

Claudio was still alive –
The Duke then made his way
To see the Provost there in charge,
Where he had this to say:

'Here is a letter from the Duke –
See there, his noble seal.'
The Provost looked to ascertain
That this device was real.

The letter gave strict orders
To spare poor Claudio.
The Provost said, 'What in the world
Can I tell Angelo?

'He'll want some proof of Claudio's death...
He'll want his severed head,
And it will be the worse for me
If I refuse,' he said.

But after some discussion
They hit upon a plan:
They'd send another head to him,
That of another man.

A prisoner'd been beheaded
Somewhat earlier that day –
They'd send *his* head to Angelo
And fool him in this way.

The head was sent without delay;
And then the good Duke wrote
To Angelo – and this is what
He said in his brief note.

The head was sent without delay

'I'm coming to Vienna.
Meet me at the city gate.
Tell everyone I'm coming.
Be there – and don't be late.

'And also tell my people that
If they require redress
From grave injustice, then ask me –
I'll sort out any mess.

'So let the news be spread abroad,
I want you to proclaim
That I, the Duke, am coming back.'
He signed his proper name.

Now in the morning Isabel,
Quite early, made her way
To prison so that she could see
Young Claudio that day.

The Duke, for reasons of his own
Told her, 'Your brother's dead,
Angelo had him killed last night –
Cut off his head,' he said.

'The head's been sent to Angelo.'
The Duke held nothing back,
And suddenly the world she knew
Was turned completely black.

'Unhappy Claudio!' she cried.
'Oh wicked Angelo!
How could he tell me all those lies?
How could he stoop so low?'

The Duke tried hard to calm her down,
But then he left her there.
He went away and laid aside
His friar's garb with care.

Then as the Duke he reappeared,
Acclaimed by high and low –
And waiting for him at their head
Was wicked Angelo.

And as the Duke passed through the crowd
Brave Isabel then cried:
'My Lord, please hear my sorry suit
Of how my brother died.'

She told him everything she knew –
Though Angelo cried, 'Liar!'
'You'll know I speak the truth,' she said,
'When you have heard the friar.'

The Duke then said, 'Lord Angelo
And Escalus – hold trial
To get the truth of all these things;
I'll leave you for a while.'

Angelo was very pleased
To judge in his own cause;
He could interpret how he liked
Vienna's ancient laws.

The Duke was not away for long –
Just long enough to dress
In friar's clothes – then he returned
To sort out all the mess.

Lord Escalus then asked the friar,
'Did you excite things thus?
Did you, sir, slander Angelo
And perpetrate this fuss?'

The 'friar' gazed back calmly
And said to this rebuke,
'I will not answer you, my Lord.
I want to see the Duke.'

Said Escalus, 'We'll hear you now.
Don't dare to make a fuss!
Speak to us plain and honestly –
The Duke is here *in us*.'

The 'friar' spoke out boldly.
'I blame the Duke,' he said,
'For letting this man judge the maid
He tried to get to bed.'

The 'friar' carried on to say,
'Well, I have looked around,
And I must tell you truthfully
I don't like what I've found.

'The state is everywhere corrupt,
The Duke has let things slip;
He should have stayed and not gone off
Upon his little trip.'

Escalus got really mad
To hear him speak this way.
'How dare you stand and criticise
The good Duke here today.'

He threatened him with torture,
And said, 'Take him to jail.
Incarcerate him for a while
And don't allow him bail.'

But then to his amazement
And everyone's surprise,
The Duke stood tall so all could see
And threw off his disguise.

Angelo turned ashen-faced,
His heartbeat leapt in speed,
He guessed the Duke was well aware
Of his disgraceful deed.

He knew his guilt was clear to see,
He'd lost his once good name.
'Sentence me to death,' he cried,
'And don't prolong my shame.'

'I trusted you,' the Duke exclaimed.
'But you just ran amok.
You, wretch, shall die like Claudio
Upon the self-same block.

'To you, fair Mariana
I suggest a different plan:
Go and search the whole wide world
And find another man.'

But Mariana up and said,
'I crave none else, my Lord.'
She begged for Angelo's base life,
She went quite overboard.

'O lend your pleas to mine,' she said
To gracious Isabel,
'The noble Duke will spare his life
If you will plead as well.'

Without delay, good Isabel,
Dropped down upon her knees.
To those of Mariana
She added her own pleas.

She said, 'I think he was sincere
Until he looked on me;
For Heaven's sake, show mercy
And set the sinner free.

'My brother was shown justice
In a twisted kind of way,
The thing for which he died he did –
This fact I can't gainsay.'

The Duke said, 'Well now, Angelo,
Be sure to love your wife,
For her fine words and pleadings
Have surely saved your life.'

Immediately his eyes grew bright,
For he was in the clear.
He took his sweet wife's hand in his
And then he called her 'Dear.'

The Duke then summoned Claudio
And to his sister said,
'Here's your lamented brother – see,
He is not really dead.'

Isabel was overjoyed.
The Duke's kind face was set –
'Claudio,' he said severely,
'You must wed Juliet.'

He pardoned Claudio right there,
Then turned to Isabel:
'Give me your hand, fair lady,
For I do love thee well.'

Isabel was free to marry,
She put aside the veil;
So there's a happy ending
To a nearly tragic tale ...

Except to say that Isabel,
Who was so fine and good,
Set such a great example
Throughout the neighbourhood

That no girls lived unmarried
With their boyfriends anymore:
They eagerly took husbands all –
And thus obeyed the law!

...no girls lived unmarried
With their boyfriends anymore

A soothsayer in the crowd called out,
'Beware the Ides of March'

JULIUS CAESAR

Our tale is set in ancient Rome
And opens on a street
Where common people often choose
To chat awhile and meet.

And so it was that one fine day
The working folk of Rome,
Came to greet great Caesar
Who once again was home.

They cheered him as he came along –
As far as one could tell,
They thought he was the greatest
And truly loved him well.

But the Roman crowd was fickle,
As soon we will discern;
They could be swayed this way and that –
Their mood could quickly turn.

But on this day as Caesar walked
A path was quickly cleared,
The crowd was pleased to see him
And to a man they cheered.

As, family and friends in tow,
He passed beneath an arch,
A soothsayer in the crowd called out,
'Beware the Ides of March.'

'What man said that?' great Caesar cried.
'Now quickly clear a space,
Set him at once before my eyes,
I wish to see his face.'

They pulled the man from out the throng.
Said Caesar, 'Speak again,
What have you got to say to me?
Now make your meaning plain.'

'Beware the Ides of March,' he cried.
Caesar sighed an angry sigh:
'He's but a dreamer, let him go –
And let us pass on by.'

The proud procession moved away
But two men stayed behind:
Cassius and Brutus tarried –
The pair were of one mind.

But each was wary to disclose
To the other what he thought,
Though both had reservations
About Caesar and his court.

They spoke in verbal riddles,
But then they heard a shout,
Brutus exclaimed, 'What's that I hear?
What's all that noise about?'

They heard more shouts and whooping then
And many a raucous cheer,
Till Brutus asked, 'What is the cause
Of all this noise we hear?

'I fear the Roman people
Have done a silly thing;
I fear that now they're choosing
Our Caesar for their king.'

Cassius asked, 'Now tell me,
Is this something that you fear?'
Brutus said, 'It surely is,
Though I hold Caesar dear.'

Cassius felt emboldened when
He heard him speak this way,
And so he shared his private thoughts
And had these words to say:

'Great Caesar is as human
As any man I know,
And yet the way he carries on
You would not think it so.

'I saved him from the Tiber once,
Rome's river, deep and wide;
I rescued him from drowning –
In truth, he nearly died.

'And then there was another time,
Whilst on a great campaign,
When on the eve of battle
Right in the heart of Spain,

'He shook from fever and cried out,
"A drink, for mercy's sake!"
His limbs grew weak, his face was wan –
This so-called God did shake.

'And yet, despite these weaknesses,
His ego has unfurled
And like a great colossus
He bestrides the narrow world.

'And we, his mere underlings,
He treats like worthless dregs;
We petty men just crawl about
Beneath great Caesar's legs.'

Thus Cassius to Brutus spoke
To court his vanity:
'You too are great as Caesar is,
Or so it seems to me.

'It's really a disgraceful thing,'
(He said this with a sigh)
'That such a man as Caesar
Should rise so very high.

'It makes the River Tiber flow
All turbulent with foam
That this one mortal man alone
Controls the might of Rome.'

Now this was dodgy ground indeed,
For this was treacherous talk
And Brutus down this dangerous road
Was very loath to walk.

So all he said was, 'Let me think
Of all you've had to say,
I will consider carefully
What we've discussed today.

'But I'll say this – I'd rather live
Within a humble home
Than live in such conditions
As today exist in Rome.'

Cassius nodded slowly then.
'I'm glad,' he slyly said,
'My words have set this train of thought
A-running through your head.'

And then with great commotion
Came Caesar back again.
He walked along most proudly,
His followers in train.

When he saw Cassius standing there,
He said, 'That man's a crook,
He seems so dark and dangerous
And he has a hungry look.'

Then Caesar passed along his way.
Brutus, to quell his fears,
Asked Casca, 'Can you tell me, please.
The cause of all those cheers?'

Casca replied, 'Mark Antony
Did offer him a crown,
Not once but thrice, and every time
Great Caesar turned it down.

'Mind you, I had the feeling
That he wanted it a lot.
I think his inclination was
To take it like a shot.

'When Caesar turned it down again,
The third and final time,
The crowd went really crazy –
They thought it quite sublime.

'They hooted, cheered and whistled,
With such stinking breath
That Caesar fainted quite away
And almost choked to death.'

'He's epileptic,' Brutus said.
'His health's not very sound –
But tell me what he had to say
When he at last came round.'

'He said, "It's my infirmity."
The crowd all cheered the more;
Their love seemed undiminished
From everything I saw.'

Casca, Brutus, Cassius then,
Each went their separate ways,
But each had much to ponder
Throughout the coming days.

The way great Caesar acted now
Quite shook them to their roots.
In truth they thought that he'd become
Just too big for his boots.

The seeds of discontentment had
Been planted in their heads,
And now they'd not be able
To sleep easy in their beds.

They feared the power of Caesar
As gradually it grew,
And each considered carefully
What might be best to do.

At night, as thunder roared above,
Cassius and Casca met,
Bare-headed, in an empty street –
And both got very wet.

Said Casca, 'I have heard today
The most alarming thing:
Apparently the senate plan
To make our Caesar king.

'They plan it for tomorrow,'
Said Casca with a frown.
'That's when they mean to give this man
A fair imperial crown.'

'This action,' Cassius replied,
'By these most stupid knaves,
Will place us all in heavy chains
And turn us into slaves.'

All his words came flying out,
He choked upon his bile –
Caesar was a tyrant then,
A man completely vile.

Casca grasped his hand at this.
'Stand with us,' Cassius said,
It was very clear he planned
To see great Caesar dead.

'Come with me on this instant,
Come with me now I say;
We must at once to Brutus
And see him right away.

'For I believe he also fears
This unannounced occasion,
But he'll support us both, I know,
With eloquent persuasion.

'He's loved by all the people,
His virtue shines so bright;
If once they see he's with us
They'll think our cause is right.'

Meanwhile upon this angry night
Good Brutus paced the floor;
His conscience troubled him a lot,
His eyes were red and raw.

He asked himself repeatedly
What in the world to do,
He loved his dear friend Caesar,
And believed this love was true.

But greater was his love for Rome,
The greatest love of all,
And he had always answered to
The Roman people's call.

He knew for sure that Caesar
Had good and noble roots,
He didn't act the tyrant –
Had no such attributes.

He told himself that though these traits
In Caesar weren't yet there,
If they insisted he was king,
Then all would need beware.

And as he paced the marble floor,
Alone within his home,
He decided Caesar's death
Would be the best for Rome.

And then he heard a knocking
Upon his outside door;
Casca and Cassius entered in
Together with four more.

They were Metellus Cimber,
Trebonius, Cinna too,
And Decius was there as well –
And each one Brutus knew.

So these were the conspirators
Who now were very keen
To murder – yes – the greatest man
That Rome had ever seen.

So these were the conspirators

They all shook hands most solemnly
And each of them agreed
The death of Julius Caesar
Was a very pressing need.

Then Decius spoke up and said,
'It is our common will
That Caesar is the only one
Whom we will plan to kill.'

Cassius replied, 'Mark Antony,
Is Caesar's greatest friend,
And he would speak against us, so
Should meet the self-same end.'

Said Brutus, 'Killing Antony
Would be quite wrong to do.
He's but a limb of Caesar –
Let's not be butchers too.

'We only kill great Caesar
For Roman liberty;
We don't need Antony's demise
In order to be free.

'Could we kill Caesar's spirit –
Leave his body here intact –
This for me would be the best
And most ennobling act.

'But alas, his blood must flow;
We'll act in this bold way.
But do it not in anger –
Then everyone will say

'We carved him as a dish for Gods,
We slew on noble grounds;
We didn't hack him into bits
Fit only for our hounds.

'We'll show the Roman citizens
Envy was not our cause:
We did it for the love of Rome
And to uphold her laws.

'We'll be described as saviours,
All Romans will applaud;
The thanks of every common man
Will be our just reward.'

Cassius said, 'Will Caesar come
To the Capitol today?
For he's grown superstitious –
That might keep him away.'

Said Decius, 'I'll get him there.
Just put your trust in me.
I'll flatter and persuade him,
He will be there, you'll see.'

And in another part of Rome
Caesar was wide awake.
His wife had woken with a cry.
'Oh help, for heaven's sake.'

She'd cried, 'They murder Caesar!'
So he too paced the floor –
For now his rest had been disturbed
He knew he'd sleep no more.

Calphurnia, his loving wife,
Now joined him in the night.
'That awful dream,' she softly said,
'Has given me a fright.'

She asked if Caesar planned to walk
Through crowded streets that day.
He answered her, 'I must go out,
I cannot hide away.'

For he was Julius Caesar,
The greatest Roman ever.
Would he cower within his house
And act afraid? No, never.

He said, 'I find it very strange...
I've often wondered why
So many men are so afraid
That one day they will die.

For now his rest had been disturbed

'I'm not afraid, so I will go
And trust in what will be.'
'Oh, say you're sick,' Calphurnia cried.
'Oh, please do this for me.'

But Caesar wouldn't heed her words,
Though she was in a state,
And he was ready to set off
When Decius came at eight.

And then the others all arrived.
They said, 'We've come for you.'
Caesar was so pleased to see
That Brutus had come too.

They set off for the Capitol
And on arriving there
Caesar saw the soothsayer
Standing in the square.

'The Ides of March have come,'
Triumphant Caesar said.
'But not yet gone,' the man replied,
And gently bowed his head.

Artemidorus – an old man –
Attempted to give warning,
But Caesar said, 'I have no time
To read these things this morning.'

He walked into the senate –
The plotters entered too.
They were nervous and on edge
At what they planned to do.

The business of the day commenced
But it was all a sham,
For they were just a pack of wolves
And Caesar was the lamb.

They bowed and scraped to Caesar
Till the moment Casca cried,
'I've had enough of fancy words,
It's time that Caesar died.'

He leapt upon poor Caesar
And stabbed him with his knife.
Then they all drew their knives as well,
Intent to take his life.

Caesar's blood in torrents flowed,
His toga turned bright red.
Then he saw loyal Brutus:
'What! You as well,' he said.

This was the final straw for him,
'Caesar gives up,' he cried.
He fell by Pompey's statue
And there it was he died.

He fell by Pompey's statue

Some of the dumbstruck senators
Cowered with fear and shock.
But Brutus said, 'Don't be afraid,
Don't start to run amok.

'For Caesar got above himself,
That's why he had to die.'
Cinna yelled out, 'Liberty!
Let this now be our cry.'

Cassius asked, 'Where's Antony?'
Trebonius then cried,
'He ran away unto his house
The moment Caesar died.'

The servant of Mark Antony
Came walking through the door;
It was clear that he was shocked
By everything he saw.

But yet he spoke and bravely said,
'My master bade me come
To ask if you'd explain to him
This deed that's turned him numb.

'Just guarantee his safety
And give good reasons why
Great Caesar has been slaughtered,
Why he deserved to die,

'Then he will love you, Brutus,
More than his friend who's dead –
So will you help my master sort
The muddle in his head?'

Brutus said that Antony
Would find a welcome there,
That he could come and have no fear,
His mind quite free of care.

The servant fetched Mark Antony,
But he could only stare
At Caesar's bloody body
Simply lying lifeless there.

He said, 'Oh, mighty Caesar,
How sad it is to know
That after all your triumphs
In the dust you lie so low!

'If I should live a thousand years
I'd choose no better time
Than this to die right here with you
Along with this foul crime.'

Brutus said, 'Mark Antony,
Please don't make any fuss;
And, most of all, you must not beg
For your demise from us.

'Though we must seem like traitors
Who've done a dreadful thing,
It was not right that Caesar here
Should ever be made king.

'We shall explain our actions to
The crowd who wait outside,
And then we'll give you reasons why
Bold Julius Caesar died.'

Antony seemed to acquiesce –
He told the bloody band,
'I'm sure that you're all very wise,
So let me take your hand.'

He went around the little group
And as he did he said,
'Forgive my action, Caesar,
Though I see how you have bled.

'You were Rome's greatest leader;
You were noble, bold and good,
Yet you were hunted down and slain –
A brave stag in a wood.'

Antony, despite these words,
Declared he was their friend:
'I'm sure in time I'll understand
Why Caesar met this end.'

He said, 'I ask but one small thing,
Let me take Caesar, pray,
Into the public market place,
And let me speak today.

'He was my friend and I should speak
To all of Rome for him.'
But Cassius breathed to Brutus then,
'Do not indulge this whim.

'He'll move the Roman masses,'
Whispered Cassius in alarm.
'His words could stir the people up
And cause us serious harm.'

Brutus cautioned, 'I'll speak first
And justify our action –
That will allay the growing fears
Of any angry faction.'

They carried Caesar's body then
Into the market place;
Antony and Brutus too,
Each went to make his case.

Now, as we know, the citizens
Of Rome held Caesar dear,
So they were straining at the leash
With eagerness to hear

What Brutus and Mark Antony
Would say to them that day
Of why their Caesar had to die
In such an awful way.

Brutus was the first to speak –
His manner was intent.
(I'll give you just the general thrust
Of Brutus's argument.)

He said, 'To friends of Caesar,
Those who held him in great awe,
I say I loved brave Caesar,
But I loved our Rome much more.

'Would you rather Caesar lived?
You know how he behaved.
If he were still alive, it's fact,
We all would be enslaved.

'I know he was a valiant man;
For this I feel contrition.
The reason that I slew him was
To stay his great ambition.

'For Roman freedom – just like me –
You'd be prepared to die.
So tell me if I gave offence –
I pause for your reply.'

Every Roman there agreed
With all that Brutus said,
And to a man they cried that Rome
Rejoiced with Caesar dead.

He said, 'I leave you citizens,
So Antony can speak –
But I'm prepared to kill myself
If that is what you seek.'

'No, live Brutus – live we say,'
The crowd all yelled as one.
'Every Roman here today
Agrees with what you've done.'

Brutus said, 'I'm going now
But beg you all to stay
And listen to Mark Antony
And all he has to say.'

Brutus left amid great cheers;
He quickly quit the scene,
And Antony stepped forward
To the spot where he had been.

He stood before the people;
His eyes were full of tears.
He said, 'Friends, Romans, Countrymen
Now lend to me your ears.

'I come to bury Caesar;
Not to sing his praises.
I know but little of the issues
Gallant Brutus raises.

'Brutus claims he showed ambition
As only tyrants can,
This must be true – for Brutus is
An honourable man.

'But Caesar was my greatest friend;
I answered to his call.
They say he was ambitious,
But I ask you, one and all,

'When Caesar won great treasure
From all his many wars,
Did he show blind ambition?
Did he ignore our laws?

'No – he brought the treasure back;
He brought it back to Rome.
Would a greedy, selfish man
Bring all this bounty home?

'And when I asked him to be king
Did he just grab the crown?
No – on three occasions
You saw him turn it down.

'I don't argue with good Brutus;
I wouldn't stoop so low.
I simply tell you what I feel;
I tell you what I know.'

Of course, all this was clever,
A well thought-out attack.
And then Mark Antony broke down,
His voice began to crack.

The people saw his anguish –
They said that all along
Perhaps great Caesar had been right,
And suffered dreadful wrong.

Once recovered, Antony
Addressed them yet again:
'Now listen to the goodness
Of brave Caesar who lies slain.

'I say to every one of you:
If you have tears to shed,
Then shed them when I show you how
Our noble Caesar bled.'

'If you have tears to shed'

He showed them Caesar's toga,
He said, 'This hole was made
By Casca's dagger – this one here
Was made by Cinna's blade.'

He showed them Caesar's body –
A bloody, awful mess.
The crowd reeled back in horror
And evident distress.

'Oh, noble Caesar!' they all cried.
'Oh, what a bloody sight!
Let no traitor stay alive;
They all must die tonight.'

Mark Antony cried, 'Countrymen,
Hold on – before you go
To finish off these tyrants, for
There's more that you should know.

'Just wait a few more moments.
Be quiet – keep quite still,
For in my hand I have with me
Our dear Caesar's will.

'And in it he bequeaths his wealth:
To every one of you
A pile of golden coins he gives.
See how his love was true.

'And all his private walks as well,
His orchards, arbours too –
He's left them all forever
For you Romans to walk through.'

Now by this time the gathered throng
Were very far from quiet.
They shouted, screamed and punched the air...
Yes – they were fit to riot.

'Kill Cassius and Brutus too,
And burn down Casca's home,
To save the world from villainy,
And our beloved Rome.'

So in this subtle manner
Mark Antony had found
A way to sway the people
And to turn their passions round.

As the angry mob rushed off,
Their cry 'Not words – but force!',
He said with calmness to himself,
'Things now must take their course.'

Then a servant came and said,
Octavius – Caesar's son –
Had just arrived in Rome and that
The plotters had all run.

They, riding now like madmen,
Before it was too late,
Sought to escape by reaching
The city's eastern gate.

Antony listened and then said,
'I'll see Octavius now.'
The servant left his master
With a low respectful bow.

So battle lines were quickly drawn.
The plotters would collide
With the friends of Julius Caesar –
Those on the opposing side.

Octavius and Antony
Were keen to get revenge;
They vowed the death of Caesar
By these cowards to avenge.

Brutus and sly Cassius had
Their loyal forces too.
They had little choice but now
To see the whole thing through.

The armies met at Philippi
Each spoiling for a fight,
Determined by a clash of force
To prove whose cause was right.

The battle raged this way and that
And it was hard to see
Who had the best advantage, or
Who would the winner be.

But Antony's great army
Began to win the day.
It seemed to Cassius fighting that
There really was no way

Their side could be the victors; they
Were everywhere assailed.
The desperate cause they'd followed had
By now completely failed.

He thought, 'I am a coward;
It really is quite wrong
For me to go on living here –
I shall not tarry long.'

He called Pindarus to him.
Pindarus said, 'My Lord.'
And Cassius said, 'Good fellow, come,
Relieve me of my sword.

'I took you for my prisoner
In Parthia, years ago;
I could have killed you there and then –
But this I think you know.

'Instead I made you promise that
You'd carry out each task
That it became my fancy
At any time to ask.

'So now with this, my trusty sword,
There's one more thing to do,
When in my cloak I hide my face
You then must run me through.

'This sword helped kill great Caesar.
Now turn its blade on me,
And with this thrust, Pindarus,
You are then my slave set free.'

Pindarus struck his master down –
He did not long delay –
Then said, 'I'll flee this country.'
And quickly ran away.

It was but shortly afterwards
That Brutus also saw
His only choice was suicide,
For they had lost the war.

He said to Clitus, 'Hold my sword,
For me to run onto.'
But Clitus said, 'Not for the world
Will I do that for you.'

And so he asked Dardanius,
But the answer was the same.
Then, turning to Volumnius,
He quietly called his name.

He said, 'I know my hour has come;
It's time to meet my end.'
Volumnius with horror said,
'That's no task for a friend.'

'It's time to meet my end'

So Brutus unto Strato said,
'Come to my side, I pray.
Then hold my sword right out like this,
And turn your face away.'

Strato said, 'Give me your hand,
Then fare you well, my Lord.'
He looked away as Brutus turned
And fell upon his sword.

And with his dying breath he said,
'Proud Caesar, now be still.
I didn't kill you, my old friend,
With half so good a will.'

Octavius and Antony
Found Brutus lying there,
They treated him with great respect
And proper funeral care.

Antony of Brutus said,
'I grieve to see him fall.
He truly was of Roman men
The noblest of them all.

'The others envied Caesar,
But Brutus understood
That Caesar tried in everything
To do the greatest good,

'For Brutus, of all people,
Did what he thought was right;
He acted out of duty,
And not with any spite.

'He killed him for the sake of Rome –
That's why he hatched his plan.
And so I say: tell all the world
This Brutus was a man.'

Octavius said, 'It's truly sad
That Brutus had to die,
But now tonight his noble bones
Within my tent will lie.

'So call a halt to battle,
And let us then away
To celebrate the victory
That we have won today.'

*The fairest-looking creature
That the world has ever seen*

ANTONY AND CLEOPATRA

At the end of Julius Caesar,
That very tragic play,
Octavius and Antony
Had boldly won the day.

They'd conquered all at Philippi,
Their adversaries had fled,
And Brutus and sly Cassius
Lay on the ground, both dead.

Octavius and Antony
With true victorious zeal
Sat down then at a table
And cut themselves a deal.

They both agreed that first of all
They'd have a super feast,
Then Antony would take in hand
The Empire in the east:

Greece and Egypt principally,
Both regions far from home.
He'd be in total charge there – but
Octavius took Rome!

And all the western provinces
He added to his realm.
So, once agreed, this meant, of course,
There were two at the helm.

This never is a good idea –
Ambitions grow so large
That they can clash and cause dissent –
Just *one* should be in charge!

And this is where our story starts –
Mark Antony's away,
Enjoying Egypt's luxuries,
Passing every day

With lovely Cleopatra,
Who is ancient Egypt's Queen,
The fairest-looking creature
That the world has ever seen.

Antony loves her fervently,
But some say, in disgust,
He sets aside his duties
To satisfy his lust.

But now the lovers enter
And we can truly judge
If this is true, or if some folk
Just bear a nasty grudge.

With pomp and with a flourish
They sweep into the hall,
A truly striking couple,
Adored by one and all.

Their presence casts a fiery glow
On everything around.
The court falls into silence;
No-one makes a sound.

Cleopatra speaks – she says,
'If you love me, tell me sir,
The true extent of this your love.'
Antony thus answered her.

'Love that can be measured
Has little worth at all,
Even beggars count their worth,
Although such worth be small.'

'I'll put a limit on your love,'
She said as she contrived
To play with him – but then she ceased
For messages arrived.

The messenger spoke up and said,
'News, my Lord, from Rome!'
Antony showed great disdain –
He thought, 'Another tome

'From young Octavius Caesar,
Can't he leave me alone!'
'I bet,' said Cleopatra,
'It's from Fulvia, that crone.'

She thus dismissed his loyal wife,
And then went on to say,
'Or from that young, scarce-bearded boy,
Octavius, I'll lay.'

Antony ignored the message,
'May Tiber deluge Rome!
I do not care – this is my place,
Not languishing at home.'

Cleopatra taunted him
But there was just no cure
For love like his, and as she teased
It heightened her allure.

Antony took the Queen's fair hand
And left the room with her.
But from this brief encounter
We can see just how things were!

And now we open a new scene
Within the sumptuous court,
Much bantering is going on –
It's all just verbal sport.

But now the Queen approaches,
Concern has given birth
To worried thoughts – for Antony
Is not disposed to mirth.

His manner now has altered,
Thoughts of Rome engage his head.
'Have you seen brave Lord Antony?'
The Queen then curtly said.

'My Lord approaches as we speak,'
Came back the prompt reply,
'And also there's a messenger
Who waits for him close by.'

Antony then entered,
He nodded to the Queen;
All but the messenger and he
Then exited the scene.

The serious message that he read
Said Fulvia, his wife,
Had fought against Octavius
And now discord ran rife.

She had joined her brother
And in one fateful hour
They'd challenged young Octavius
And tried to grab his power.

The messenger brought further news:
Parthia, Rome's great foe,
Had overrun fair Syria
And planned to overthrow

Roman power in the East –
Under Antony's rule...
He clenched his fist and then exclaimed,
'I've been a silly fool!

'It's time I broke away from here,
From these Egyptian fetters;
If I do not there's bound to be
Another load of letters.'

He hardly had expressed these words,
They'd barely left his mouth,
When someone else approached who said,
'I have just hurried south

'To bring sad news to Antony.'
He slowly bowed his head.
'My Lord, I've come to tell you
That Fulvia is dead!'

The messenger departed.
Enobarbus came along,
And seeing Antony's distress
He said, 'Is something wrong?'

Enobarbus was a friend
And, though the news was bleak,
Antony was pleased to have
Someone with whom to speak.

And so he said, 'I have to leave,
And get away from here;
The Queen has brought me only woe
And misery, I fear.

'I wish I'd never seen her face,
For she has made me shirk.'
Enobarbus said, 'But then
You'd not have known this work.

'You'd not have seen her beauty –
So wonderful!' he said.
Antony then blurted out,
'My Fulvia is dead!'

Enobarbus, hearing this,
Said, 'When old robes are worn
You change them for fresh garments –
That's how new love is born.'

Of course he was implying
That Antony could wed
Queen Cleopatra, now he'd heard
His own poor wife was dead.

'Enough of this,' said Antony.
'There's more bad news from home,
For word has come that Pompey's son
Is now a threat to Rome.

'This new young upstart plans to bring
The Empire to its knees;
He's raised a mighty navy
And now controls the seas.

'I must away, but first of all
I will inform the Queen;
She should be brought right up to date
With this fast-changing scene.'

He went to Cleopatra –
She'd not listen to a word;
It seemed she didn't want to hear
The things that had occurred.

She said he had deceived her
When he told her he must go;
He couldn't get a word in,
She didn't want to know.

Then finally she listened,
He said, 'You misconceive –
Young Pompey is a threat to Rome.
That's why I have to leave.'

And then he said, 'My Fulvia's dead.'
He spoke without emotion;
He didn't seem to show an ounce
Of husbandly devotion.

Cleopatra cried, 'False love!
Should not a husband cry?
I see how it will be received
If Egypt's queen should die.'

She really let him have it,
She gave him a hard time.
You would have thought poor Antony
Had carried out a crime.

Finally he'd had enough.
'I'll leave you now,' he sighed.
'O courteous Lord, one word I ask –
O hear me now,' she cried.

'May victories attend your way,
And Gods all bless your sword...
And think of Cleopatra –
For we have loved, my Lord.

'Your honour calls you from me;
Be deaf to all I say.
Take my blessing with you...
And now, my Lord – away!'

≈≋≈

Antony hurried back to Rome
And met Octavius there.
When first they met they proved to be
A most suspicious pair.

They wouldn't speak or even look
The other in the eye,
Till Lepidus spoke up and said,
'My Lords, I beg, draw nigh.

'Don't let unruly tempers
Interfere in this way
With all the pressing problems
That we have to solve today.'

A most suspicious pair

''Tis spoken well,' said Antony,
'Let's be of one accord.'
Octavius then bowed his head,
'Welcome home, my Lord.'

They then began to parley,
Octavius went first:
He was so full of anger
He was almost fit to burst.

He said, 'Your dead wife, Fulvia,
Consumed by so much hate,
Took up arms against me,
Thus threatening the state.

'You sent me no assistance,
Though she was in the wrong.
It seemed to me her husband did
Support her all along.'

Antony apologised
For showing no respect:
'My sin was of omission
And I admit neglect.

'My mind was poisoned, I'm afraid,
The hours tied me up,
As I drank much too deeply
From Egypt's jewelled cup.'

Octavius accepted this
And, though he'd been quite riled,
Decided it was for the best
If they were reconciled.

He believed this was no time
To take a heavy stand,
So going up to Antony
He shook him by the hand.

Agrippa then spoke up as well.
'I now propose,' he said,
'Octavia and Antony,
To seal this bond, should wed.'

Octavia was the sister
Of Octavius, you see –
They had been given these like names
When at their mother's knee.

Antony agreed – he felt
It was the thing to do
But feared the strong reaction once
His Cleopatra knew!

And now to Egypt where we find
The Queen upon her throne;
She hasn't been too happy
Since being on her own.

A messenger from Rome comes in,
The first one that she's seen.
He walks towards the throne and bows –
'I bring you news, my Queen.'

Excited Cleopatra said,
'Make sure the news is good,
If you place value on your life.'
The messenger just stood.

He was too scared to give the news
After the words she'd said,
For he believed there was a chance
He now could end up dead.

But then the Queen controlled herself.
She said, 'Tell me the news.'
The messenger was frightened,
But how could he refuse?

'Speak up!' she said impatiently
But still he seemed to tarry,
Then blurted out, 'Lord Antony
Has been coerced to marry.'

Well! Cleopatra hit the roof.
'What's this you say?' she said.
'Lord Antony is married!
Sleeps in Octavia's bed?

'I'll kick your eyes, I'll have you whipped,
I'll pickle you in brine,
I'll pull the hair from off your head,
You foul, dissembling swine!'

'Gracious madam,' he replied,
'This plan, I did not hatch;
I merely bring the news to you –
I did not make the match.'

'It's you who've moved me to this rage,'
Fair Cleopatra cried.
'You've lived too long, my sorry friend,
And now it's time you died!'

She drew a knife to kill him,
She'd really lost her cool.
The poor man saw her coming
And, being no-one's fool,

He quickly scampered from the room,
A timely thing to do.
But then the Queen calmed down and called,
'Come back, I won't hurt you.'

And once again he ran away

And once again she asked him if
The news were really true.
When he confirmed that it was so
Her temper flared anew.

And once again he ran away
In fear of fresh attack
But then she shouted to her maid,
'Quick! Go and get him back.

'I want him to reveal to me
What this Octavia's like.'
It is a truly fearful thing
To see great envy strike.

For angrily she cried aloud,
Through bitter, sobbing tears,
'Report the colour of her hair,
Her features and her years.

'I want to know how tall she is.'
Then quite borne down with gloom,
She asked her maid, Alexas,
To take her to her room.

She later quizzed the messenger,
And said, 'Now tell me all.'
The messenger, to play it safe
Told her, 'She's not that tall.

'In fact she's rather dwarfish,
She's certainly not young,
She really is no beauty –
And she's very dull of tongue.'

Cleopatra archly asked,
'Tell me about her gait.
Does she parade with majesty?
Now give it to me straight.

'But keep in mind whom you address –
You look on majesty.'
The messenger knew what to say,
It was so clear to see.

He said, 'She has no feeling,
She does not show emotion;
She stands just like a statue
And seems to have no notion

'Of what goes on around her;
She has a funny gaze –
She seems to live the whole of life
In a perpetual haze.

'When she walks she creeps along,
Her voice is deep and low.'
Cleopatra smiled and said,
'That's all I need to know.

'You are a first-class messenger.
I'll give you work to do.
Yes, I am now beginning
To really take to you!'

⚜

Octavius and Antony
Now both arranged to meet
Young Pompey for a conference.
They were prepared to greet

The enemy who'd taken arms
Against the Roman might.
And Pompey said on seeing them,
'We'll talk before we fight.'

He knew that he was master
With his navy on the seas,
But when it came to strength on land
The others held the keys.

Seeing Antony returned
Made youthful Pompey waver;
To have this seasoned soldier back
Weighed greatly in their favour.

And so he was prepared to talk –
The Emperors were too.
They quickly came right to the point:
'We will concede to you

'Sardinia and Sicily,
But you must then agree
To rid us of all pirates
Who terrorise the sea.'

The deal appealed to Pompey, who
Was grateful for the lands;
So with this meeting over
The three of them shook hands.

The leaders then departed;
Enobarbus stayed behind.
He scratched his head most knowingly
And said, 'I'll bet we'll find

'That Antony's new marriage
To Octavia, won't last.
The whole thing was agreed in haste,
Too quickly, much too fast.

'I would lay money on the fact
That Antony will wish
To go as soon as possible
To his Egyptian dish!'

Meanwhile on Asia's rolling plains
A war is being waged
By Antony's bold captain,
Who is totally engaged

In conflict with the Parthians –
You'll recall they'd made a raid
On Syria, which land they'd tried
To sneakily invade.

This captain called Ventidius,
Who was both wise and brave,
Was very firm in his resolve,
He was intent to save

The country from invaders,
And in a mighty brawl
He sent the Parthians packing,
The whole lot, one and all.

When they had won, a soldier said,
'Permission, Sir, to speak.
Let us pursue and crush them now,
This foe is really weak.

'What a victory we could win
With just one single blow.'
But Ventidius wisely said,
'Don't let ambition grow.

'Antony's not with us
And to win so great a prize
When he is absent from the field
Would really be unwise.

'It wouldn't do at all, you know,
To gain too great a fame;
We'll just report our victory
And do it in his name.'

What a clever captain!
He knew how to survive.
Not to take the credit
Was the way to stay alive!

Antony to Athens went –
Octavia went there too –
But thoughts of Cleopatra
Stuck to his mind like glue.

And he complained at last to her:
'Octavia, I have heard
Your brother has insulted me –
Of this I have had word.

'He also fights with Pompey
When we said that we'd be friends.
What is Octavius up to?
What are his devious ends?

'Go to Rome, Octavia,
And speak to him,' he pleaded.
At first she was reluctant,
But finally conceded.

She departed then for Rome
To act as go-between;
Once she had gone sly Antony
Set sail to see the Queen!

He sailed for Alexandria.
Cleopatra waited there –
And once again the man was caught
In Cleopatra's snare.

They made themselves the rulers
Of the country all around;
It was a perilous path on which
The two of them were bound.

Octavius raised an army:
Antony did the same.
To beat the other into pulp
Was now each Emperor's aim.

Egypt's army boarded ships,
And Cleopatra too.
She said, 'My sixty vessels,
Are prepared, my love, for you.'

Antony gave grateful thanks,
Then swiftly sailed away
To meet the massive Roman fleet –
And so began the fray.

They met quite close to Actium
And fought upon the sea,
But halfway through the battle
Cleopatra turned to flee.

Her sixty ships, the royal fleet,
Just turned and sailed away;
It wasn't clear to anyone
Why they declined to stay.

Antony, disheartened then,
Relinquished all exertion;
He was completely baffled by
His lover's brisk desertion.

He gave up the battle,
Ignored the heavy cost;
Since Cleopatra now had fled
He thought that all was lost.

They met quite close to Actium
And fought upon the sea

He had but one obsession,
Which was to follow her;
He had no thought for anything,
Love was his only spur.

His navy was defeated
But he was not concerned;
His thoughts were only on the Queen –
And how his passion burned!

He sailed to Alexandria
And there he found the Queen.
He said, 'Where have you led me?
What does your cowardice mean?

'For I am so ashamed to own
That I gave up the fight;
I lost the will to carry on
When Egypt's fleet took flight.

'I found it hard when I espied
Their disappearing tails.'
She cried, 'I am so sorry, please
Forgive my fearful sails.

'I little thought you'd follow
Or mimic my defection.'
He said, 'My sword is weakened by
The bonds of deep affection.'

She broke down then in tears and said,
'How could it come to this?'
He said, 'One act will make amends –
Revive me with a kiss.'

They kissed in passionate embrace,
And Actium was forgiven,
But it is fair to say a wedge
Between their love was driven.

Octavius has now arrived
In Egypt – camp is made
Quite close to Alexandria,
A nice spot in the shade.

He had pursued Mark Antony,
And now receives his terms
From Antony's young messenger
Who openly confirms

That Antony is quite aware
His situation's dire,
And so respectfully requests
Permission to retire.

Antony has also said
That he is very keen
For Cleopatra to remain
As Egypt's noble Queen.

Octavius will not agree
To Antony's new plan,
And privately he told himself,
'I won't deal with this man.'

When the envoy made his way
To Antony once more,
His master said, 'What did he say?
Now tell me what's the score.'

He didn't like the answer
And said, 'Go ask the Lord
To meet in single combat –
We two, just sword on sword.'

Of course, Octavius refused.
He said with dismal sigh,
'The ruffian should realise
That is no way to die.'

Octavius sent Thidias
To see the Queen alone.
He said, 'My master bids me say
That he has always known

'You little care for Antony,
Though he is always near,
And though you hold him very close,
You did this out of fear.'

Cleopatra answered him,
With just the one word, 'Oh!'
Quite what she was implying
Was very hard to know.

Was it because she was surprised,
Or said sarcastically,
Or was she acting in the hope
That they would set her free?

But as they talked, brave Thidias
Believed he could appeal
To the proud Queen's ambitions
And quickly strike a deal.

He said, 'Abandon Antony...'
(Appealing to her pride)
'Then you can keep great Egypt
By joining with our side.'

Cleopatra said with guile,
'You tell Octavius this:
I take his conquering hand in mine
To honour with a kiss.

'I'll lay my sceptre at his feet,
And there I too will kneel.'
Thidias was quite certain that
The two had struck a deal.

'It is the wisest course,' he said
'Give me your hand, fair Queen.'
But as he took it Antony
Burst wildly on the scene.

'What treachery is this?' he cried,
As he came through the door.
'So now you are betraying me,
You cheap unfaithful whore.'

Then turning on poor Thidias
He very quickly gripped
His arm – and said, 'You, my good friend,
Will be severely whipped.'

Thidias was taken out
And given a sound whipping.
Without a doubt the judgement
Of great Antony was slipping.

You always treat an envoy
In a most respectful way;
It really was a dreadful deed
The Emperor did that day.

Then Antony told Thidias
'I punished you for backing
Octavius instead of me.'
Then he sent him packing.

When he had gone, Mark Antony
Collapsed in deep despair;
He feared that Cleopatra had
Completely ceased to care.

But she replied most vehemently –
She cried, 'Hear what I say.
If that is so, then flies can eat
My people as their prey.'

She finally convinced him.
He said, 'I'm satisfied.'
Now Antony felt really sure
His mistress had not lied.

Octavius and Antony
Now each got ready for
A monumental clash of arms:
They both prepared for war.

The fearful conflict which took place
Was bloody as could be;
They waged their war upon the land
And also out at sea.

And at the height of battle,
Out on the raging sea,
The Egyptian fleet, just as before,
Turned on their tail to flee.

Antony went wild with rage,
It drove him quite insane.
He cried, 'This foul Egyptian queen
Has welched on me again.'

It's hard to give a reason why
She fled again to shore.
Did she still love Mark Antony
Yet love great Egypt more?

Did she believe the fight was done,
That Antony had lost?
And did she think she'd save herself,
However high the cost?

No matter what her reasons,
She turned around and fled;
Left on his own, poor Antony
Cried to the gods and said,

'I fought these wars for Egypt
And for this fickle Queen.'
He felt that he had every right
To fully vent his spleen.

He vowed that he would kill her,
Although his love still burned,
Despite his passion for the Queen
His mood had really turned.

Octavius then gave orders:
'Find out where Antony hides;
Let no self-harm befall the Queen –
I'll have no suicides!

'Bring Antony before me here,
I do not want him dead.
He'll go to Rome in captive's chains –
And may that cool his head.'

He planned to make Mark Antony
A prisoner back home,
And then parade him through the streets
Of unforgiving Rome!

And so we now approach the end:
Cleopatra fled
Into her palace – 'Take me to
The Monument,' she said.

This was a mighty edifice,
Constructed to endure
A siege of fearsome magnitude;
It really was secure.

Once there she sent a message
To Antony which said,
'The Queen has ended her poor life.
God help the Queen, she's dead.'

When Antony was told the news
He railed in disbelief;
As the appalling truth sank in
He wallowed in his grief.

He cried, 'Oh Cleopatra,
You were my life, my sun,
But now you have departed hence,
The long day's task is done.

'I cannot live without you,
I must quit this earthly scene;
I'll not be far behind you –
I'm coming now, my Queen.'

He told his servant, Eros, then,
'I beg you, set me free!
Take my sword and use it
To put an end to me.'

Eros loved Mark Antony;
He could not kill his Lord.
But Antony insisted
So he lifted up the sword.

'Shall I strike you now, my Lord?
I beg you please to tell.'
And Antony replied, 'At once.'
So Eros said, 'Farewell!'

Then plunged the sword into himself,
And said with his last breath,
'Thus I escape the sorrow
Of causing my Lord's death.'

'Brave Eros!' Antony in shock,
And in shame withdrew.
'You have the nerve to do yourself
The deed I could not do.'

He grabbed the blood-soaked sword.
'I'll run to death,' he said.
'Just as a bridegroom hurries home
Into his new wife's bed.

'And so, young Eros, now I die,
Your pupil, not your Lord.'
And with no further dallying
He fell onto his sword.

But then a moment later
A new messenger arrived,
This one informed Mark Antony
His loving Queen survived.

He was very close to death
But said, 'I beg you take
This dying man unto the Queen –
Do it for mercy's sake.'

They took him to the Monument
To see the Queen once more,
But, fearing for her safety, she
Would not unlock the door.

And so they hoisted him with rope
To a window high above,
And thus he was united for
The last time with his love.

And there he died, wrapped in her arms.
She begged, 'My love, please stay.
I cannot live in this dull world
When you have passed away.'

'And so, young Eros, now I die'

143

But he was gone forever.
She vowed that she'd die too,
Declaring, 'I have little choice
Except to follow you

'Into the secret house of death.
I'll make death proud of us;
I'll die in Roman fashion,
With style but with no fuss.'

She would not trust the Romans.
Whatever did they plan?
And as for young Octavius,
She didn't like the man.

So finally she decided
That she would end her life.
You'd think she would have chosen
To end it with a knife.

But no – her chosen means of death,
To rule out all mistakes
Was to request a basketful
Of very poisonous snakes.

They brought the serpents to her,
She bared her heaving chest,
Then took an asp and held the snake
Most firmly to her breast.

'Come now, you mortal wretch,' she cried,
'Be now my deadly knife,
And use those sharp envenomed fangs
To take away my life.

'The knot that binds me to this earth
Now sever – set me free!'
She grabbed another asp and cried,
'I'll take more help from thee.'

Then took an asp and held the snake

The second asp bit savagely.
'Oh, Antony,' she cried.
Then she collapsed across the bed,
And that is where she died.

When Octavius heard the news
He had these words to say:
'Because she was of royal blood
She chose to die this way.

'But she shall sleep with Antony,
A truly noble pair,
And none more famous in the world
Than those two lying there.'

And that is where she died

He kicked the Duke, called Senior, out

AS YOU LIKE IT

It doesn't always follow
That siblings will agree;
Sometimes the strife between them
Is clear for all to see.

It happens at all levels,
To rich and poor alike,
There is no way of telling
When jealousy will strike.

For once there was a famous duke
Who ruled a part of France;
He had a selfish brother
Who led him quite a dance.

For this mean brother, Frederick,
Full of nastiness and bile,
Stole his brother's dukedom
By skulduggery and guile.

He kicked the Duke, called Senior, out
At once onto the street
With just the clothes upon his back
And not a scrap to eat.

It's really hard to credit that
This man would stoop so low,
But truthfully it must be said
He wasn't nice to know.

The Duke thus driven from his court
So wickedly by force,
With some few faithful followers
Set his unhappy course

For Arden forest, fair and green,
Far from any town,
There to make some kind of life –
And there to settle down.

This they did, and soon they saw
That there was much to please –
They liked the open air and found
They loved the life of ease.

No pomp and courtly customs
To bother them at all,
In fact they found life in the wood
Was really quite a ball.

They savoured long, hot summer days,
They watched the dappled deer
Who, getting used to them, grew tame
And often grazed quite near.

So when they had to slaughter one
In order to get meat,
They all felt very sorry –
But of course they had to eat.

And then the cold, dark winter came
With fierce and biting wind,
Their only barrier being hides
Of beasts that they had skinned.

The Duke said, 'I can stand all this –
The winter's bitter mood –
But what I find so hard to take
Is gross ingratitude.

'The treachery of my brother
Is very hard to bear,
How could he take my dukedom?
How could he even dare?'

But then by moralising
He'd do everything he could
To see the good in all around,
The blessings of the wood.

Duke Senior had a daughter
Who'd stayed behind at court
For Frederick, the usurper,
Had had a selfish thought:

He'd make the daughter, Rosalind,
Remain – so she could be
A friend to his own daughter
And keep her company.

The girls ignored the quarrel
Between the silly lads;
They still remained the best of friends
Despite their warring dads.

Frederick's daughter, Celia,
Was very kind and good
For she had tried so hard to do
The very best she could

To make poor Rosalind happy
When her face fell in a frown;
She tried to lift sad Rosalind
When she was feeling down.

And then one day as Celia
Was trying hard to bury
All young Rosalind's sad thoughts
And make her blithe and merry,

A message came from Frederick –
It came with all dispatch –
Asking if the girls would like
To see a wrestling match.

Although it seems unladylike
For them to watch such sport,
Wrestling was a pastime loved
By everyone at court.

So off they went most eagerly
To see this bloody sight –
It seemed to promise it would be
A most diverting fight.

The coming bout was to be fought
By two men badly matched,
To look at them it seemed that one
Would quickly be dispatched.

A powerful and a massive man
Had just that day been billed
To fight a youth, whom all there thought
Was certain to be killed.

For he had no experience
And though so bold of heart,
He hardly knew a thing about
The ancient wrestling art.

His opponent, it was said,
Was deadly to behold,
He'd slain so many in the ring
And knocked a lot out cold.

When Frederick saw the girls arrive
He said, 'Now you've appeared
I beg you speak to that young man,
Tell him we're all a-feared

'That he'll be slaughtered here today;
To fight would be unwise.
We have no wish to see him die
Right here before our eyes.'

So Celia addressed the youth,
She said, 'I beg you sir,
Please do not risk your life like this.'
He took no heed of her.

Then Rosalind herself spoke up
In kind and gentle way,
'Resist this madness, dear kind sir,
And do not fight, I pray.'

His eyes met hers and in a flash
A love began to grow.
But in a modest, graceful tone
He said, 'My answer's "no".

His opponent, it was said,
Was deadly to behold

'I'm sorry to displease you both,
Two ladies fine and fair,
And I am grateful for the fact
You choose to show such care.

'Give me your gentle wishes
And if I die right here,
Do not lament my passing,
But I beg, be of good cheer.

'For if I'm killed, then so be it;
I'm not afraid,' he said.
''Twould be of little consequence
If I should end up dead.

'And if I lose my life today
No friends will grieve for me,
For I've no friends in all the world
Nor loving family.

'And the space my body takes
Within this world,' he said,
'Can better far be filled, I'm sure,
By someone else instead.'

The wrestling match got under way.
Rosalind, for her part,
So moved by what the youth had said
Completely lost her heart.

The youth fought well and bravely
And in truth it must be said,
The kindly words from both the girls
Spun round inside his head.

It gave him strength and courage that
He didn't know he had,
And so he fought incredibly
For an untutored lad.

He quickly gained the upper hand
To everyone's surprise,
And then before the startled crowd –
Yes, right before their eyes –

He knocked the expert wrestler down.
Stretched out upon the floor,
He was completely out of it;
The man could fight no more.

Frederick jumped onto his feet,
'Bravo, young sir,' he yelled.
No-one there could quite believe
The expert had been felled.

Frederick had the happy thought
To take the youth in care,
For he liked the lad he saw
All breathless, standing there.

'What is your name?' asked Frederick.
'Orlando,' he replied,
'Sir Rowland de Boys' youngest son,'
He said with quiet pride.

Frederick's face became a mask,
It went a ghostly white;
His tender feelings for the youth
Now quickly turned to spite.

His banished brother, Senior,
Had been Sir Rowland's friend,
Until the bold Sir Rowland
Had met a sorry end.

Frederick hated hearing any
Reference to that name,
But still the valour of the youth
Impressed him all the same.

So as he left in angry mood
Reflecting on his brother,
He said, 'Orlando, how I wish
That you were someone other.'

Rosalind was kinder though;
She was so pleased to hear
Orlando was the son of one
Her father held so dear.

Orlando was astounded
By Frederick's remark;
It seemed unkind, unwarranted,
Abruptly cruel and stark.

But Rosalind and Celia both
Spoke to Orlando thus,
'We're sorry that Duke Frederick
Made such an awful fuss.'

Rosalind took a golden chain
From round her neck and said,
'Wear this, good sir, I beg you.'
Then placed it o'er his head.

When the girls were on their own
Asked Celia, 'Is it true,
That you now love Orlando?
Perhaps he loves you too.'

Before her friend could answer
Or utter anymore,
Duke Frederick came crashing in
And slammed the chamber door.

Sir Rowland, as we've heard, had been
Duke Senior's favourite friend,
And thinking of the pair of them
Made Frederick descend

Into the depths of black despair
Because he knew for sure
The people loved the banished duke –
At least, from what he saw.

They favoured Rosalind as well,
Felt sorry for her too;
They pitied all her suffering
And all that she'd been through.

So now his hate boiled over –
On Rosalind it fell.
'Leave the court today,' he cried,
'You're banished now as well.'

Celia pleaded with him,
'Oh, father, change your mind,
For I will miss dear Rosalind,
Please don't be so unkind.'

'Don't be a little fool,' he yelled,
'For all the time she stays,
The people love her more than you,
They much prefer her ways.

'When she is gone, you will appear
Much better than before.
I'll not relent, my mind's made up,
Don't argue anymore.'

Now Celia was a decent girl,
And loyal, good and true.
She said to Rosalind, 'Don't fret
I'll come along with you.'

That night the two young girls crept out
And through the palace garden;
They went to join the banished duke
Among the trees of Arden.

Before they went, young Celia said,
'I think it would be wise,
For safety's sake, to make our trip
Dressed up in a disguise.'

They put on simple country clothes
To carry out their plan,
Celia dressed in woman's garb,
Rosalind as a man.

They would tell everyone they met
They shared the self-same mother,
They were a dear devoted pair,
A sister with her brother.

They called themselves by different names
To aid their little game:
Rosalind chose Ganymede,
Aliena, Celia's name.

They asked the court fool, Touchstone,
'Are you prepared to be
Our travelling companion
To keep us company?'

He agreed – in truth he was
Quite under Celia's thumb –
He said, 'I'll follow where you go,
I shall be glad to come.'

The three set off for Arden,
A long way it was too,
And how to find Duke Senior,
They really had no clue.

When they finally arrived,
Tired out, quite on their knees,
Celia said, 'I've had it,
Let's rest beneath these trees.'

As they rested there awhile
A shepherd walked close by.
'Where can we find some food and rest?'
Asked Rosalind with a sigh.

The man was but a servant.
'My boss will help,' he said.
'He has a cottage that he'll sell
And give you meat and bread.'

The three set off for Arden

They gratefully accepted –
They'd stay there for a while
Until they found Duke Senior
Who'd free them from their trial.

We'll leave the girls right there a while,
For it's now time to know
The fate of the courageous lad
Whose name was Orlando.

He's also in the forest,
So let's go back a trace,
In order to explain just how
He turned up in that place.

Orlando had a brother –
First of Sir Rowland's boys,
Who when the old man passed away
Soon set about his ploys.

His father'd told this brother,
'Oliver, I charge you
Look after young Orlando
When my old life is through.

'Give him an education,
Watch over him, be true.
I trust your noble nature,
For I depend on you.'

But when Sir Rowland up and died,
Oliver said, 'A fool,
Would waste his money on this kid
By sending him to school.'

But even though untutored,
Orlando soon became
A fine and decent person,
Most worthy of his name.

And for this reason, Oliver
Grew jealous of the lad;
The way he used Orlando
Would have made their father mad.

Oliver had put him up
To fight the fearsome guy
Whose hands had been the ones to cause
So many men to die.

He'd arranged the wrestling match
And hoped that he'd be killed.
Imagine how annoyed he was
His wish was not fulfilled.

Orlando was victorious!
Oh, what a great surprise,
That he should win when set against
A man of such great size!

Oliver's anger overflowed...
'I'll sort him out for sure.
I'll burn his lodgings while he sleeps
And lock his bedroom door.'

'Twas lucky for Orlando
That Oliver was heard
By one good, faithful servant,
Who noted every word.

This servant's name was Adam
And he told him of the plan.
'You must leave right now,' he said,
'Get going while you can.'

So Orlando left at once,
And Adam followed too;
Running off just seemed to be
The only thing to do.

They fled to Arden forest
But on arriving there
So short they were of food and rest
It was too much to bear.

For Adam spoke of dying,
(He was close to giving up)
'I need some food to eat,' he cried,
'And something good to sup.'

Orlando went in search of food
And entering a glade,
He saw a band of merry men
Who had a banquet laid.

It was Duke Senior and his men.
Orlando drew his sword,
He didn't think they'd give him food
Of their own accord.

He felt he'd have to steal to eat,
Thus his aggressive mood,
But the Duke with kindness said,
'Sit down and have some food.'

Orlando said, 'Before I eat
There's one who's hungry too;
A poor old man who's followed me
Must eat before I do.'

The Duke said, 'Fetch him instantly.'
Orlando disappeared.
And when he'd gone the Duke remarked,
'How often life is weird.

'These grim and woeful pageants
Before us are unfurled,
Like shows within a playhouse
As vast as this wide world.'

Jaques, one of his brave men,
Who thought himself a sage,
Declared, 'Without a trace of doubt
All the world's a stage.

'And men and women players
On their respective stages,
And each man in his time plays parts,
To suit his seven ages.

'First he plays the infant
Who's wont to puke and mewl,
Then the whining boy who creeps
Unwillingly to school.

'Next he plays the lover,
Full of sighs and woes,
Then the soldier, bold and brave,
As off to war he goes.

'Then he acts the serious man,
Wise words and gross fat belly,
Then he shrinks and his meek voice
Is wobbly, like jelly.

'Second childhood – final scene –
Approaches with great haste,
It brings on mere oblivion:
No teeth, no eyes, no taste!'

Now Rosalind and Celia,
Who were settled in the wood,
Kept seeing carvings on the trees
They little understood.

They saw these carvings everywhere,
On trees, both far and wide,
And passionate love poems
On twigs were also tied.

The carvings spelt out 'Rosalind',
The poems were addressed
To Rosalind, and in them all
The author there professed

She was the sweetest maiden
That he had ever known,
And in his breast, a fervent love
Had recently been sown.

As they pondered on the words
One fine and sunny day,
They came upon Orlando
Who was passing by that way.

He of course saw 'Ganymede',
A handsome looking male,
And Aliena – a young maid –
Along the woodland trail.

He stopped to pass the time of day,
For little did he think
That here was Rosalind, on whom
He'd used up so much ink.

Rosalind's young heart beat fast
To see him once again,
But still she thought it would be wise
If she were to refrain

From saying who she really was –
So all she said was this:
'Have you observed the carvings?
They're very hard to miss!

'They're everywhere you chance to look –
I tell you, my good sir,
This lover must love Rosalind,
He surely dotes on her.

'He has a silly sickness,
Though I'm sure his love is pure;
He needs some help to handle it,
I could suggest a cure.

'If I knew just who he was,
I'd help him to recover.'
Orlando there and then confessed,
'I am this poor lover.'

Rosalind (or Ganymede)
Said, 'This I now propose:
Come to our cottage every day
And there I will disclose

'The way to cure this love of yours,
For I'll pretend to be
The lovely Lady Rosalind;
You'll speak of love to me.

'I'll act the love-shy maiden –
It won't take long, you'll see,
Before you feel ashamed of love,
And this will set you free.'

Orlando had but little faith
In this, her remedy,
But said, 'I'll come along and try,
I'm sure it can't hurt me.'

He liked this young and pleasant lad –
In fact he thought he looked
Quite like the Lady Rosalind
By whom he had been hooked.

And so from that day onward
Orlando made his way
Unto the shepherd's cottage
And practised what to say

To his beloved Rosalind,
Used all those silly words
That lovers whisper all the time –
They were like courting birds.

And he loved every moment,
Though he thought it just a game;
It was such fun for him to say
His Rosalind's fair name.

He also liked to speak aloud
(Not knowing, in her sight)
All those little compliments
In which young men delight.

Of course he didn't realise
The one to whom he spoke
His words of love was Rosalind –
He only saw a bloke.

Orlando had told Rosalind,
'Duke Senior lives quite near.'
Though she had not rushed off to see
The father she held dear.

But then one day while walking
On a woodland path she knew,
She bumped into her father
Who said, 'How do you do?'

The Duke did not know who it was,
And so he said to her,
'Pray tell me of your parentage.'
She said, 'My gracious sir,

'I come from a good family
That's well known to be fine,
And so I think it's fair to say
I'm born of noble line –

'As noble as yourself,' she said,
In bold immodest style.
Her answer quite amused the Duke,
He could not help but smile.

'To think this shepherd-boy believes
He has a pedigree
That can compare with mine,' he thought,
'That really couldn't be.'

When Rosalind saw her father
Was fit and all a-glow,
She thought, 'I'll wait a day or two
Before I let him know

'That I am also in the wood,
There is no rush to tell.
I shall explain in all good time
How I am here and well.'

One day Orlando, setting off
To see his Ganymede,
Came suddenly upon a man
Asleep but in great need.

A large green snake had come along
And found a way to wind
Its body round the poor man's neck,
And thus they were entwined.

But at the youth's approach the snake
Had quickly taken fright;
It slid away into a bush
And disappeared from sight.

You'd think that this was pretty bad
But there was worse to come,
For what Orlando now perceived
Made all his limbs go numb.

A lioness was crouching
In the bushes there close by –
It seemed the sleeping man for sure
Was destined now to die.

A lioness was crouching

The lioness was waiting
For the man to come awake,
And when he'd fully woken
Was the time that she would make

A swift and murderous attack
With one almighty leap,
For lions won't destroy their prey
While it is fast asleep.

Orlando stood there mesmerised,
He felt his bold heart race,
And then he looked down at the man
And gazed into his face.

The person sleeping on the ground
Clearly was no other
Than someone whom we've met before:
Orlando's wicked brother!

It was the awful Oliver.
Orlando sighed a sigh –
'Perhaps I should just leave him here
And let the tyrant die.'

But brotherly affection
Came rushing to the fore,
All thought of leaving him to die
Went flying out the door.

He drew his sword, the lion fought
With its great gnashing jaws,
And then it caught Orlando's arm
And tore him with its claws.

Blood rushed from the wound, but he
Began to fight again,
And thrust his sword with such great force
The lion lay there slain.

The noise made Oliver wake up;
He saw the awful sight:
His brother and the lion
Engaged in mortal fight.

He saw that brave Orlando
Had risked his life to save
A scheming, worthless brother,
A coward and a knave.

Once the lioness was dead
He called his brother's name;
Borne down with great remorse he was,
And overpowering shame.

He repented there and then
His conduct in the past;
He now embraced his brother while
His tears flowed thick and fast.

Orlando was quite overjoyed
And readily forgave;
His brother thanked him for his life,
He said, 'You were so brave.'

And from that moment onward
Their affection grew and grew,
They put aside all quarrelling
And they began anew.

But as he held Orlando close,
He said with much alarm,
'Look here, you're badly wounded,
We must bind up your arm.'

Orlando said, 'I feel so weak,
So while I rest, I ask
If you will do a favour, and
Perform a little task.

'Please go and tell friend Ganymede
I cannot come today.'
Oliver said of course he'd go
And hurried on his way.

He reached the woodland cottage, where
He said, 'I've come to tell
That your good friend Orlando
Isn't feeling well.'

He recounted everything:
How brave Orlando fought,
And how despite his own cruel ways,
The selfish end he'd sought,

Orlando had forgiven him.
He said, 'How I regret
The way I've wronged my brother, and
I will not soon forget,

'How freely he forgave me,
And put my wrong aside.'
Celia, as she listened, found
That she could barely hide

The way she was beginning
To fall in love, right there
With Oliver, who showed remorse
And genuine despair.

Rosalind, when she was told
Orlando had been hurt,
Collapsed right there upon the floor
In all the muck and dirt.

It seemed most strange that this young man
Should swoon upon the floor;
When Rosalind came round, she said,
'It was pretence, no more.'

Oliver again returned
To Orlando and he said,
'I've fallen for a shepherd girl
And now I hope to wed.'

Orlando said, 'I counsel you
Most strongly, do not tarry –
Ask the lady for her hand
And then you two can marry.'

When later all was settled,
To gentle Ganymede
Orlando said, 'Would Rosalind
Were here so I could plead

'Her hand in holy marriage,
For her to be my wife.
I swear it is the only thing
I really want from life.'

'If that's your wish,' said Ganymede,
'Then put away your sorrow;
I'll arrange for you to wed
Fair Rosalind tomorrow.'

Orlando, very doubtful,
Thought it all was just a joke,
That Ganymede was acting like
A rather silly bloke.

But he insisted that he'd bring
Fair Rosalind to wed.
'I'll use some magic that I've learnt,'
He very archly said.

'If that's your wish,' said Ganymede

The following day they gathered,
With everyone excited.
The Duke was there as well, of course,
For he had been delighted,

When told his daughter would appear –
Oh, what a great surprise!
But he suspected Ganymede
Might just be telling lies.

Then Ganymede said to the Duke,
'My Lord, I wish to know,
Would you agree for Rosalind
To marry Orlando?'

The Duke replied, 'Oh, that I would.'
And Ganymede then said,
'Orlando, would you too consent
To also being wed?'

'With all my heart,' came his reply.
Then Ganymede withdrew,
Removed her man's attire – became
The Rosalind, they knew.

She didn't linger very long,
She did not keep them guessing;
When she returned she knelt and asked
Her father for his blessing.

They had a double wedding,
There was no time to lose,
And then a messenger arrived
Who brought them joyful news.

Frederick did now repent
The error of his ways,
And made a declaration
That he would spend his days

In a religious order.
He said, 'When I get there,
I'll kneel in contemplation
And devote myself to prayer.'

The first act of his penitence
Was forthwith to return
The dukedom to his brother;
And then he would adjourn,

To life in lone seclusion –
And he did so with all speed.
Oh, what a fine conclusion!
What splendid news indeed!

Thus all was for the better –
'As you like it', you might say.
For everyone prefers it when
A tale turns out this way.

A melancholy monarch

184

HENRY THE FOURTH
– Parts I and II

In Richard the Second, Shakespeare's play,
The seed was deftly sown
That helped young Henry Bolingbroke
Assume the English throne.

His cousin Richard, then the King,
Was a capricious bore
And hadn't cared that England
Was slipping into war.

His realm was ill at ease,
With discord everywhere;
Civil war was on the cards
But Richard didn't care.

Then Henry had a falling out
With Richard, who got riled,
And said, 'I've had enough of you.
Henceforth you'll be exiled!'

With Henry gone the King began
To spread all kinds of smears
About his cousin – who then stayed
Abroad for six long years.

Then Henry's noble father died,
John of Gaunt, he passed away –
And once the old man breathed no more,
Upon the following day

Richard grabbed the dead man's money
To fund an Irish war.
Henry went ballistic
When he was told the score.

For this was his inheritance,
It wasn't there to serve
The foolish King's indulgent wars,
By God, he had a nerve.

He raised an army and returned,
Urged Richard to a fight;
He was determined to regain
What things were his by right.

Richard was defeated,
Henry's following was huge –
Richard hurried off to Flint
And there he took refuge.

But he was apprehended
And agreed to abdicate,
Though he refused to recognise
His crimes against the state.

To Pomfret castle he was hauled
And locked within a tower.
Then Henry took control of things;
He grabbed all royal power.

But still some nobles argued,
'Why should Henry be in charge?'
They said he was above himself,
His plans had grown too large.

So then they hatched a cunning plot
To have Henry removed,
And there were many in the realm
Who heartily approved.

It failed and they were caught; it seemed
Richard was involved.
So Henry's counsellors advised,
'Kill Richard – problem solved!'

But Henry just told Richard
He would no longer brook,
These plots against his person
Then he let him off the hook.

But then a little later on
Sir Piers Exton overheard
Henry discuss his cousin –
He called him, 'That jailbird!'

He said, 'Do I not have a friend,
At least one person dear,
Who'll offer some assistance –
Rid me of this living fear?'

Sir Piers thought, quite reasonably,
He wanted Richard dead,
But this was really not the thing
In angry Henry's head.

Sir Piers thought it an order
And so, without delay,
He jumped onto his horse and rode
To Yorkshire, that same day.

And there he murdered Richard –
Oh what a bloody thing!
But this now left the path quite clear
For Henry to be king.

And even though he was distraught
About the awful deed,
He knew that he must take the crown –
There was a pressing need,

For England now required a king,
It was the thing to do;
He couldn't leave a vacuum
For discontent to brew.

So although he was upset
By the murder in the north,
He let himself be duly crowned
King Henry the Fourth.

And this is where the play begins
That bears King Henry's name.
He now sits upon his throne,
Taking all the blame

For King Richard's murder.
Shrouded all in gloom,
A melancholy monarch,
Henry sits there in his room.

He is most unhappy,
He's a very troubled king,
Weary and dispirited,
Borne down with everything.

For though he can't condone the way
Sir Piers rode roughshod,
And killed a king whom all had seen
Anointed once by God,

He still felt very thankful
To have Richard out the way,
Yet this didn't stop him thinking
That there'd be a price to pay.

So as he sat reflecting,
His mood completely bleak,
He finally was moved to words,
And thus began to speak:

'I did not wish my cousin dead,
It isn't what I meant,
And for this awful murder I
Most heartily repent.

'Sir Piers made an error,
He didn't understand –
He's brought a deed of slaughter
On me and on this land.

'But now all this must cease,
We'll heal all wounds and sores,
No more brother fighting brother,
No more civil wars.

'And to wash away this blood
From off my guilty hand,
I'll make a pilgrimage this year
Unto the Holy Land.

'We'll raise a mighty army,
One that never yields,
And then we'll drive the pagans from
The sacred, holy fields.'

But as the King decided
That plans would now be laid
To go and save Jerusalem,
And make this great crusade,

Messengers arrived at court
In a very worried state;
They brought disastrous news, and so
Crusading now must wait.

Royal forces had been vanquished
By the Welsh – who had then taken
Mortimer, a prisoner;
The King was badly shaken.

His general thus captured,
This was a crushing blow,
But then another messenger
Declared, 'My Liege, I know

'Of happier news from Scotland,
Because I beg to tell
There's been a great rebellion
Up in the north as well.

'But brave and daring Hotspur,
The King's most loyal friend
Has fought the rebels hand to hand
And brought it to an end.'

'Bravo to Harry Hotspur!'
The King cried out. 'Bring wine,
We'll drink his health – oh, how I wish
That worthy lad were mine.

'If only it were proven
That the fairies did alight
Upon his cradle, when a child
And in the dead of night

'Exchanged him for my worthless son,
So *he* was really mine,
That Harry Hotspur was my son –
And so the next in line.

'And not that useless reprobate –
My son, who's never here,
Who spends his time in taverns,
Quaffing wine and swilling beer!'

So having heard King Henry
Complain about his son,
We'll go to where this lad, Prince Hal,
Sleeps off a night of fun.

We find him at his lodgings,
He's there with his best friend,
A man whose great indulgences
Are truly without end.

I speak of Sir John Falstaff –
He's sixty and he's fat,
He has a bloated, ruddy face
And lots of ready chat.

He loves all forms of pleasure,
He's game for anything:
He likes the ladies of the night,
He likes to drink and sing.

There's hardly any silly prank
That Falstaff hasn't done,
And any moment of the day
He's up for having fun.

When his great booming laugh rebounds
Around a noisy room
It causes all to laugh with him,
And chases off all gloom.

He has a way of talking
In a deep and winning brogue,
That cleverly conceals the fact
That he's a cunning rogue.

For he is into thievery –
A bad example for
A royal prince of England
Who should respect the law.

Prince Hal should not be wasting
His precious time like this,
But hanging out with Falstaff
Is a pleasure not to miss.

Now old Sir John is coming round,
He says when half awake,
'Whatever is the time of day?
Tell me, for goodness' sake.'

Prince Hal then chuckles merrily,
'Whatever do you care
What time the clock is telling,
While you are lying there.

'Unless the hours are cups of wine,
The minutes food to eat,
And clocks the tongues of willing whores
You hope that you will meet.

He's a cunning rogue

'And the dials the signs of brothels,
The sun a gorgeous tart,
Dressed in a crimson, low-cut dress
And with a giving heart.

'If this, therefore, is not the case,
Then tell me sir, I pray,
Why in the world should you require
To know the time of day?'

Falstaff laughed out loud and said,
'You're not wrong there, my lad –
We thieves do all our work at night,
Not in the day, by gad.

'But when you're king, you'll have no truck
With thieves, I will be bound.'
'What none?' Prince Hal replied with mirth,
And made a mocking sound.

And so the banter carries on
In this light-hearted way,
It was the way they spent their time
On every single day.

But then another chap comes in –
Poins is this fellow's name –
And he takes but a moment
To join the verbal game.

He makes great fun of Falstaff,
He calls out, 'Hey, beanpole,
How go negotiations,
With the devil, for your soul?

'You sold it him Good Friday last
Just for a glass of wine.'
Falstaff laughed as if to say
That all was going fine.

Then Poins announced, 'I've hatched a plan
To make us all some dough
From pilgrims bound for Canterbury –
We'll rob them as they go.'

Falstaff cried, 'A great idea!'
Hal thought they'd come to grief
And strongly remonstrated,
'What me? Become a thief?'

Sir John replied, 'Now come on, Hal,
And lend a helping hand.'
Prince Hal cried out, 'You know I can't,
You surely understand.'

Falstaff then became annoyed,
He said, 'I'll say one thing,
For this I'll be a traitor
When you become the King.'

He left them in a huff, but then
Once safely out the door,
Poins said to young Hal laughingly
'Right, now I'll tell you more.

'For I've a mind to play a joke
On that bad-tempered lout,
And when I tell you of my plan
I know you'll fall about.

'We'll let fat Falstaff and his friends
Rob pilgrims on the pike,
But we'll stay safely out of sight
And let them make their strike.

'For we'll arrange a meeting place
And then we'll fail to show;
They'll do the robbery on their own
While we are lying low.

'And once they've got the money,
We two will then appear,
Dressed in working clothes and masks,
We'll fill their hearts with fear.

'For they are cowards, one and all,
And so with no to-do,
We'll steal the money from them there.'
Hal said, 'We are but two!'

Poins cried, 'If that old bumbler,
That silly fool, that fraud,
Does not run off with all his friends,
Well then I'll eat my sword!'

Where was the fun in all of this?
Well, Poins went on to say,
'When we all meet at supper,
The rogue will find a way

'To make himself a hero
When he gives us both the gen;
He'll swear upon his life he fought
With over thirty men.

'He'll tell us how he drove them off,
He'll give it all a spin:
How many blows he suffered
And the tight spot he was in.'

They laughed out loud and heartily
Just thinking of the sight
Of their fat friend, Jack Falstaff,
On the ensuing night –

How he'd do everything he could,
Try every trick he knew,
To make his lying load of bunk
Appear completely true.

So then Poins said, 'Adieu, my Lord.'
And left Hal all alone.
The prince's thoughts grew sombre
Now he was on his own.

He said, 'For just a little while
I'll go along with this,
And wink at all this nonsense
Though it is quite amiss.

'I'll imitate the glorious sun
Who lets the looming clouds
Conceal his beauty for a while
Behind their murky shrouds.

'So when he once again breaks through
In shafts of warming light,
His very presence, that's been missed,
Becomes a welcome sight.

'Thus it will be with this fair prince,
For in a little while,
I'll put aside this worthless life
And moderate my style.

'And when this sudden change occurs,
When I improve my ways,
I'll be the meek recipient
Of much high-vaulted praise!

'For, like a chrysalis, I'll break
And change my playboy past.
Then the world will all acclaim:
"He is a prince at last –

'We knew it all along.
It was just young Hal's joke;
He's a proper royal prince,
A really first-class bloke." '

·ૐ·

While all of this was going on
There's trouble back at court,
For Hotspur and some others
Had now come south – but brought

No prisoners along with them –
A most unusual thing:
It was the normal practice
To give them to the King.

The King demanded prisoners
To ransom them for cash,
As Hotspur didn't bring them
They were heading for a clash.

The King thinks artful Hotspur
Has other fish to fry;
He thinks that he is worried
That Mortimer might die.

You will recall that Mortimer
Was taken prisoner too,
Captured fighting for the King,
As Henry rightly knew.

Welsh rebels held him captive,
But Henry wouldn't pay
A ransom for the Earl's release;
He had the nerve to say,

'It's clear he is a traitor
He's guilty of great sin –
He should have kept on fighting,
Not simply given in.

'Why ever should I help him?
Now someone give me reason –
Why I should pay good money out
And why reward high treason?'

This made Hotspur wild with rage,
For Mortimer, you see,
Was brother to his own dear wife...
Of course, he wants him free.

The King thinks that he's trying
To do a crafty trade:
Mortimer for prisoners –
And that is what has made

King Henry very cross with him –
His anger knows no ends –
So they became great enemies,
Who once had been good friends.

Hotspur storming from the room
Decided on one thing:
To form alliance with the Scots
And then to fight the King.

What a different kind of youth,
What a ball of fire,
Hotspur is compared with Hal,
For now he does conspire

To take the throne of England,
His ambition does astound –
And all this time, all Hal can do
Is play and mess around!

Hotspur storming from the room

A day or two have passed, and Hal
And Poins are now both waiting
Within the Boar's Head Tavern
To give Sir John a baiting.

Falstaff and his friends, as planned,
Had stolen all the cash;
Then Hal and Poins attacked them
And made off with the stash.

So they expect old Jack's return,
And they can hardly wait,
To hear just what he has to say –
But will he tell it straight?

Hal's in a right good humour
And has some fun awhile
With Francis, a young waiter,
Who's respectful and servile.

He's been running back and forth;
Hal says, 'The lad's a hick,
A parrot knows more words than him –
This lad is really thick.'

Thereat this caused him to reflect –
He says, 'I'm not the same
As that wild fellow in the north
Who has the funny name.

'That fellow, Harry Hotspur,
So full of manly bluster,
Who's always boasting to his wife
And making her a-fluster.

'He says to her, "My darling wife
I have been out a-killing."
She replies, "Oh, Harry dear,
That really is most thrilling."

'He says, "I killed eight Scotsmen
While you were still in bed;
And there were many more of them
But they just up and fled."'

Thus young Prince Hal amused himself,
Inventing lots of fun
About young Harry Hotspur
And all the deeds he'd done.

Perhaps he was beginning
At last to be aware
That people now were starting
To studiously compare

The way he spent his princely days
With Hotspur, bold and brave,
And maybe they'd concluded now
That Prince Hal was a knave!

But at that very instant
There's a banging on the door –
This is the moment that Prince Hal
And Poins have waited for.

In comes Falstaff with his friends.
Poins said, 'So how are you?'
'A plague on cowards,' Falstaff cries,
'And vengeance on them too!

'Give me a jug of wine, I pray,
My throat is dry and raw.
What is becoming of the world?
There's honesty no more!

'I know of only three good men
Unhanged in England now,
And one of them is fat and old.'
He pointed to his brow.

Prince Hal said, 'What's the matter,
You fat, old reprobate?'
'You're cowards, all,' Sir John replied,
Still in a fiery state.

Poins said, 'Don't call me coward,
Be careful what you say.'
The knight replied, 'Give me more wine,
I've had no drink today.'

Hal said, 'You drunken villain!
You've scarcely wiped your lips
Since knocking back your last huge glass –
I still can see the drips.

'But what's got into you, fat Jack?'
Hal asked his friend, once more.
'I'll tell you, Hal,' John Falstaff said
'This morning, just we four

'Set out and stole a thousand pounds,
We did it all alone –
Because you wouldn't join with us
We acted on our own.'

Hal asked, 'So where's the money, Jack?'
Said Falstaff with a cuss,
'The cash was stolen on the road –
A hundred ambushed us!

'For two long hours we fought them,
It's a wonder we're alive,
It really is a miracle
We managed to survive.

'See here, they stabbed me through my coat,
About eight times in all.
I've cuts in other places,
Too many to recall.'

And so they bantered back and forth,
As Falstaff told his tale.
The more that Poins and Hal remarked,
The more he did regale

The company about his guile,
How boldly he had fought,
How lucky his aggressors were
That they had not been caught.

He said they were a hundred,
But then he said sixteen;
It was very hard to tell
How many there had been.

Hal said, 'I do sincerely hope
That you ran no-one through.'
Falstaff replied, 'I'm almost sure
That I put paid to two.

'Spit in my face, if you believe
That ancient Jack is lying,
But I saw two of them at least
Were on the way to dying.'

Sir John pursued with gusto
All the details of the fight,
But Hal and Poins, of course, knew well
His words were false and trite.

So finally Prince Hal came clean.
He said, 'You horse back-breaker,
You red-faced coward, hill of flesh,
You overweight old faker...'

But Falstaff interrupted
With a torrent of his own:
'You slimy eel, you ox's tongue,
You lump of skin and bone.'

But he ran out of breath, so Hal
Commenced his tale once more:
'It's time you knew the truth, old man
How we set on you four.

'We carried off the money
That you had seized, and saw
That you put up a lousy fight
When once you knew the score.

'And, Falstaff, you old coward,
You took your guts away
About as nimbly as I've seen
In many a long day.

'We heard you roar for mercy,
You threw away your staff,
And ran with the dexterity
Of a nimble-footed calf.

And ran with the dexterity
Of a nimble-footed calf

'So, my old friend, now let us hear
What clever lies you'll tell,
What explanation you'll advance
Of what we know befell.

'Come on, old Jack, speak up, we say,
For we can't wait to hear.'
After a pause John Falstaff said,
'Well, well, my friends, draw near,

'Now listen very carefully:
I swear I knew you well,
I recognised the pair of you,
And though you did propel

'Your friend who stands before you here
Into a grisly fight,
I do believe my actions were
Entirely in the right.

'For once I knew it was my Hal,
Once every doubt had flown,
You'd not expect me then to kill
The heir to England's throne.

'You know I am like Hercules
But even I would wince,
At thought of running through the heart
A noble, royal prince.

'I ran away through instinct
For a lion won't attack
A prince – of that you can be sure
And neither will old Jack.

'If I had acted differently
'Twould have been wrong and rash...
But let's get back to serious things –
I'm glad you've got the cash!'

But at that very moment
Mistress Quickly hurried in.
She was hostess of the tavern,
This bawdy house of sin.

She said, 'My prince, a messenger
Has come here from your father,
He's waiting here to speak to you.'
Hal told her, 'I'd much rather,

'That you would send him packing,
For I have no wish to speak;
Send him quickly on his way
And give his nose a tweak.'

But Falstaff went to see him
And when shortly he returned
There was no doubt that he was shocked
By everything he'd learned.

He said, 'That crazy fellow,
Harry Hotspur – him you know –
Is raising a rebellion, and
Your dad wants you to go,

'To court first thing tomorrow,
For he is very sure,
That Welsh and Scottish rebels
Are planning to make war.'

They soon returned to jolly games
And merriment once more,
But then another knock was heard
Upon the tavern door.

It was the sheriff with his men.
'They want me,' Falstaff cried.
Prince Hal turned round and said to him,
'You'd better go and hide.'

He hid behind a curtain
As the sheriff scanned the bar.
He said, 'We seek some robbers
And we know just who they are.

'One is quite notorious,
A fat man – likes his beer.'
'I can assure you,' Hal replied,
'He's not been seen in here.'

He sent the sheriff on his way.
'I'll do the best I can,
To help you solve this robbery
And apprehend this man.'

They saw the sheriff to the door
And once they were quite certain
That he had really disappeared,
They then drew back the curtain.

You'd think that Falstaff would be there
All cowering in a heap,
But this old drunken reprobate
Had fallen fast asleep.

He was stretched out upon the ground,
And all he did was snore;
He didn't give a fig that he
Was wanted by the law!

But this old drunken reprobate
Had fallen fast asleep

As ordered, on the morrow morn
Hal took himself to see
King Henry in his palace, where
The King said, 'Leave us be.'

He spoke to all his courtiers,
He said, 'It's my desire
To speak alone, with my dear son.
I wish you to retire.'

And so the lords and ladies left,
They quietly withdrew.
The King turned to his son and said,
'What can I do with you?

'It seems the very heavens
Turn their revenge on me,
By giving me a son like you
Whose manner's so carefree.

'For it is not appropriate
For one of princely rank
To carry on the way you do –
My son, I must be frank.

'You waste your time on base pursuits,
Your friends are all uncouth,
You are a disappointment –
I'm sorry, that's the truth.'

What in the world could Prince Hal say,
Yet, feigning some surprise,
He answered, 'Some of what you hear
Are really downright lies.'

The King began a lecture,
He gave his son what for,
He said, 'Wherever will this end?
Your prospects look so poor.

'My friends all think you're heading
For an almighty fall,
And all we ever hear from you
Is how your life's a ball.

'You don't attend the council,
Your brother takes your place,
You never come to see me,
You never show your face.

'You mix with vulgar people,
You enjoy yourself too much,
You are forever showing off,
You lack the royal touch.'

Hal thought the King had finished,
He thought that he was done,
But Henry still had other things
To lay upon his son.

'Why can't you be like other boys?
You always let me down;
Even Hotspur acts with style
Though he now fights the crown.'

This dressing down upset Prince Hal,
'One day, I'll prove,' he said,
'My honour is intact and true,
I'll bring you Hotspur's head.'

The King seemed satisfied with this –
How could he ask for more?
He said to Hal, 'Prepare yourself,
For we are now at war.'

And so two armies gaze across,
The one upon the other,
Once more a civil war looms large,
With brother fighting brother.

The word is out that young Prince Hal
Is quite a stirring sight,
He's all on fire for battle now
And ready for a fight.

Negotiations then take place
To try to find a way
They can avoid a bloody clash,
And so not fight that day.

Prince Hal suggests a daring scheme:
'This Hotspur,' thus he said,
'I'll fight in single combat and
Will spare all this bloodshed.

'The winner claims the victory
Of the battle here today.
I know that I can beat him,
My Lord, what do you say?'

King Henry would have none of it.
He spoke up with a frown:
'You must be joking, I'll not risk
The forfeit of my crown

'On you, an inexperienced boy,
It really wouldn't do,
For Hotspur, in a moment, would
Make mincemeat out of you.'

All parleying came to an end,
It now was time to fight;
Two armies faced the great divide,
A truly fearful sight.

And then the battle started,
And so with no delay,
It turned into a raging scene,
A tangled, massive fray.

Prince Hal was badly wounded
But he didn't think to yield;
Despite his bleeding, gaping wound
He would not leave the field.

He went back into battle and
He found King Henry there,
Fighting the Earl Douglas...
Hal cried, 'Come, if you dare,

'And cross your sword with me, proud Earl;
I swear I'll run you through,
For it is Harry, Prince of Wales,
Whom you are talking to.'

They fought – but then Earl Douglas
Turned on his tail and ran,
A cowardly example from
A would-be gentleman.

King Henry was extremely pleased
With what the prince had done,
He said, 'You have redeemed yourself;
I'm proud of you, my son.'

The King retired from the scene,
And then it was quite weird,
For almost out of nowhere
Harry Hotspur now appeared.

He said to Hal, 'I do believe
You're Harry, Prince of Wales,
And I am Harry Hotspur,
Of whom you've heard some tales.

'The time has come for one of us
To leave this blessed earth,
So let us cross our swords to find
The measure of our worth.'

Prince Hal replied, 'So be it, for
Two stars can't occupy
The self-same orbit high above,
So one of us must die.'

As they began their mortal fight
A friend came on the scene:
'Twas fat and foolish Falstaff –
Whatever did this mean?

Well, he had joined the army,
To fight there in the war;
He'd thought that it would be a lark,
He'd have some fun for sure.

'So one of us must die'

223

Falstaff cheered his friend, the Prince,
He yelled, 'Go on – attack!'
But as he urged him on, behold!
Earl Douglas came on back.

Then they began to fight as well.
'I don't like this,' Jack said,
And so he fell upon the ground
Pretending to be dead.

Douglas hurried on his way –
Prince Hal with one deft thrust
Gave Hotspur, such a mortal wound
He fell down in the dust.

'Harry, you've robbed me of my youth,'
He cried, 'But what hurts most
Is that you take all honours, lad.'
Then he gave up the ghost.

Hal looked down upon the corpse –
'Six feet of earth you need,
A kingdom was too small for you
Before this bloody deed.

'So farewell, Harry Hotspur,
You were valiant, for sure.'
Then turning round he saw Sir John
Prostrate upon the floor.

Then turning round he saw Sir John
Prostrate upon the floor

'What now, old friend, unhappy Jack,
A sad loss you would be,
If I had really doted on
All that frivolity.'

And then without a backward glance
He slowly walked away,
Poor Falstaff, lying in the mud,
Was lost for words to say.

But then he jumped onto his feet.
He said, 'Your pardon, Lord.'
And, stabbing the dead Hotspur
With his sharp and trusty sword,

He then slung the lifeless body
Across his ample back.
He carried Harry Hotspur's corpse
As if it were a sack.

But now approaching rapidly
Comes Hal – oh, what a pain!
But straightaway Sir John exclaimed,
'My Prince, look – I have slain

'The bold and mighty Hotspur.
I killed him in fair fight.
He came round the very moment
That you were out of sight.'

Prince Hal replied how sad it was
That Hotspur had to die,
And thus without a further word
Accepted this great lie.

The royal forces won the day,
And Falstaff was allowed
To claim he'd killed young Hotspur;
King Henry was so proud

Of his bold son, the Prince of Wales
He said, 'One thing, I'll lay
There seems a chance Prince Hal will make
A worthy king one day!'

The battle scarce was over when
More troubles came their way –
Rebels pooled their forces
To fight another day.

Their leaders all want action,
They're tired of idle talk,
They're led by Earl Northumberland
And the Bishop of York.

Though Henry now laments the fact
Disorder rules his realm,
His nobles give him confidence
That with him at the helm

They can defeat the rebels,
Peace will return once more,
And everyone will live within
The monarch's royal law.

The whole affair comes to a head
When two great armies meet.
Their leaders have a parley,
But Henry's leaders cheat.

The royal forces there are led
By his young son, Prince John,
Who is about to carry out
The most enormous con.

He sends the Earl of Westmoreland
To have a little talk
With an opposing leader,
The Bishop who's from York.

The Bishop has a serious list
Of grievances to make,
Complaints against King Henry, all
'Made for the people's sake.'

Westmoreland says breezily,
'These points are all agreed,
So now we have no cause to fight,
There really is no need,

'Let's each dismiss our army,
Let's call it all a day;
I'll get our monarch, Henry,
To sign all this today.'

The rebels sent their men away,
They took his word on trust,
For they were sure that Henry would
Prove honest, fair and just.

But Henry's son, the young Prince John,
In acting for his dad,
Turned out to be a devious chap,
A cunning, lying lad.

For once the rebel forces had
Disbanded, and withdrew,
The prince, who'd kept his army whole,
Then swiftly told them to

Attack and mow the rebels down;
He caught their leaders too,
And had them executed –
A rotten thing to do!

Meanwhile back in London
The King is very sick,
But he is glad to hear the news
Of Prince John's sneaky trick.

His kingdom is now safe, and he
No longer needs to fear,
But as he learns of this good news
His own demise draws near.

Retiring to his bed, he rests,
And while he's fast asleep,
Prince Hal creeps to his bedroom
To take a little peep.

He looks upon his father then
And he becomes quite sure
That Henry, King of England, now
Lives and breathes no more.

He sees his country's royal crown
Upon the pillow there;
He leans across his father
And picks it up with care.

He takes it from the bedchamber
For this is not a crime,
He truly thinks his hour has come –
It is Prince Harry's time.

But the King is merely sleeping
And when he wakes he cries
'Where is my crown, where has it gone?
Don't count on my demise.'

Prince Hal comes back into the room;
His father sees him there.
He said, 'It seems, young Harry,
That you hunger for my chair.'

Prince Hal replied, 'I never thought
To hear you speak again.'
His father said, 'I stay too long,
I see you're keen to reign.'

The Prince did everything he could
With passionate emotion,
To calm him and convince the King
Of his supreme devotion.

Then Henry said, 'Sit down, my son.
I have not long to live,
And there is some advice I wish
To very quickly give.'

He gave his son good counsel,
Hal hung on everything;
At last there seemed an even chance
He'd make a decent king.

King Henry said, 'Now take me
To my chamber; there I'll lie,
And, yearning for Jerusalem,
Will sad King Henry die.'

And so King Henry passed away –
A new king was acclaimed:
Henry the Fifth of England
Prince Hal was now proclaimed.

His coronation was arranged,
A truly great affair,
A chance for all the common folk
To cheer and shout and stare.

The glorious procession
Set forth through London town,
Towards Westminster Abbey
Where Hal would claim his crown.

And as the pageant made its way
A man stepped from the crowd –
He was enormous, fat and round,
His voice was very loud.

'God save the King, my dear sweet boy!'
It was no other than
Jack Falstaff – but the King replied,
'I know you not, old man.'

And so with this one gesture
Harry made it very plain,
He'd put aside his foolish ways –
Now was his time to reign.

This was a transformation:
Prince Hal had been dispatched,
And in his place, Henry the Fifth,
The ruler, had been hatched!

And so our story opens
With two clerics who discuss

HENRY THE FIFTH

As we have seen, the young Prince Hal,
A playboy through and through,
When he became the English King
Completely changed his view.

When he was crowned Henry the Fifth
It really turned his head,
'This is extremely serious stuff,'
He very gravely said.

He turned his back on fooling
With Falstaff all the time;
He now thought all frivolity
Was tantamount to crime.

And so our story opens
With two clerics who discuss
A matter that could cause the Church
A monumental fuss.

They are Ely's noble bishop
And Canterbury's too.
The subject of their discourse
Has put them in a stew.

They are concerned that Henry,
Like his father once before,
Is after grabbing papal lands,
Ignoring every law.

Ely's bishop thus exclaimed
Borne down and quite bereft,
'If he takes all he has in mind
There will be nothing left.'

Canterbury then replied,
'If this comes to befall,
In truth it surely must be said
'Twould drink the cup and all.'

Ely sighed, 'Oh what a trial,
On this we must confer,
What in the world can we both do
So this does not occur.'

Then Canterbury up and said,
Hope etched across his face,
'The King is of such fair regard
And now so full of grace

'That he will surely prove to be
A good and noble king
And listen with a kindly ear
To all the pleas we bring.

'For though he was a tearaway
When he was but a lad,
And though his every action caused
Distress to his poor dad,

'Once his father, that old king
Was dead and breathed no more,
At once his wildness seemed to die,
It flew right out the door.

'His total reformation
Came upon him like a flood,
And in the twinkle of an eye
He showed his royal blood.'

Ely mused, 'The strawberry grows
Beneath the stinging nettle,
So kings grow best with baser fruit
Before they show their mettle.'

Canterbury nodded then;
He said, 'All is not lost,
For I have made the King a gift
At some enormous cost.

'I've offered him a goodly sum
To put him in our debt.
It is the largest pile of cash
The Church has given yet.

'Believe in what I say, my friend,
It is a large advance,
And has been given with regard
To matters touching France.

'But more of that awhile – for we
Must now be on our way,
For France's chief ambassador
Craves audience today

'With noble Henry, our good Lord,
So let us go, I pray,
Unto the court so we can hear
Just what he has to say.'

❧

King Henry sits amid his court;
Then Canterbury comes in.
The King is pleased to see the priest
And says with winning grin,

'I wish to ask advice of you,
For France is now my aim:
May I in rightful conscience make
Upon that land a claim,

'To take the French throne for myself?
I think it should be mine.
I beg you, good archbishop,
How does your will incline?'

Well, Canterbury then began –
And how the man could talk!
From giving an opinion
He'd never, ever baulk.

The man went on and on until,
At last he said, 'It's true –
By right the royal throne of France
It should belong to you.

'And so, my good and gracious king,
The clergy give to you
More money than we have before
To do what you must do.'

Of course the wily cleric gave
This money with one hand,
In hope the other would hang on
To all the Church's land.

Henry's nobles there approved;
They thought it quite a plan.
They'd conquer France or else they'd leave
Alive no single man.

Henry was well pleased and said,
'We are within the law,
And once we've conquered France's lands
We'll win their minds, I'm sure,

'Or break them all in pieces –
So summon here to me
The French ambassador right now.
I'm eager thus to see

'What messages he brings to court;
Let's hear him speak, I pray.
What is the news he would impart
To all of us today?'

The ambassador was summoned
And when he came he brought
A message from the Dauphin,
The heir to France's court.

Then once he had delivered
The Dauphin's salutation,
He carried on to speak about
Young Henry's reputation,

Of how he was so frivolous –
Of youth's unlucky falls –
And then he offered him a gift
Of sixteen tennis balls.

This was of course an insult,
A taunt to Henry's pride;
It made the point quite clearly
And mockingly implied

That Henry should confine himself
To playing boyish games.
It was a rather subtle way
Of calling Henry names.

It was intended to convey –
No doubt of this, for sure –
The King should leave the craft of state
And weighty things like war

To grown-up men, and take himself
To childish things again.
The King replied – and angrily,
He made his feelings plain.

He said, 'The Dauphin's action seems
Designed to make things worsen,
For it insults our national pride,
Likewise my royal person.

'All that follows now will be
The Dauphin's fault alone,
For I am quite determined now
To take the French King's throne.'

He vowed that he was certain
That he acted by God's laws.
He cried, 'The King of England comes,
Mine is a rightful cause.

'So forward into battle all,
Where we will take our chance,
We have no other thought except
The thought of winning France!'

So preparations start for war;
There's fever in the air,
But Henry hears a rumour
That he should now beware,

For he has learnt that three close Earls,
Cambridge and Scroop and Grey
Are traitors to the crown and now
Are in the Dauphin's pay.

They plan to murder ruthlessly
Henry – their King and lord.
Apparently the three of them
Are all of one accord.

Henry's in Southampton
To gather forces there;
And these three Earls have been enticed
Right into Henry's lair.

They're unaware the noble King
Knows of their treachery,
They think their reputation is
Just what it used to be.

So Henry starts to play his game:
He asks Earl Scroop, 'What chance,
That we will be victorious
Against the might of France?'

'There is no doubt we shall succeed,'
Scroop says with utmost guile.
'And led by such a King as you,'
Grey says with slimy smile.

'Never was a King more loved
Or feared,' Earl Cambridge cried.
King Henry, hearing these false words,
Just raised his eyes and sighed.

He took then three commissions
And handed them around.
The three Earls grabbed the manuscripts
And read without a sound.

They thought these were their orders
For the impending war,
But each turned deathly pale to read
The words that now he saw.

They held their own death warrants,
Each clearly showed the reason:
They were accused of treachery,
Of villainous high treason.

Henry called them traitors.
'My downfall was your goal;
But you, Lord Scroop, have hurt me most –
You knew my very soul.'

They all admitted there and then
What traitors they had been,
What low and lying scoundrels –
The worst the court had seen.

Henry said, 'As for myself,
I seek no great revenge,
But for betraying England's realm,
That crime I must avenge.

'So, you shameful wretches, go
To pay for this offence.
Go to your deaths – God help you all.
Soldiers, bear them hence.'

They held their own death warrants

Boldly then King Henry said,
'The signs of war advance,
And I'll not be the English King
If not the King of France!'

We must take a detour now,
Back to old London town,
To where the King once played around
Before he wore the crown.

The Boar's Head tavern is the place
Where now we must repair,
And, if you've read Henry the Fourth,
You'll know some people there.

All Henry's former drinking pals
Are also off to war,
When worthy Mistress Quickly
Comes rushing through the door.

'Come to Sir John and quickly,'
The hostess loudly cried.
'Come with all haste, I beg you,
Come now to his side.

'For he is racked with fever;
It's awful to behold.
He may not have that long to live –
At least that's what I'm told.'

He may not have that long to live

Of course she spoke of Falstaff,
The King's old friend in fun,
That dear old fellow whom the King
Now sadly chose to shun.

Nym spoke up tersely at her words,
'Ay, since the King departed,
Poor old Jack has been bereft,
Depressed and so downhearted.'

Pistol claimed, 'Oh yes, it's so.
Jack Falstaff never thought
His friendship with King Henry
Would one day count for naught.'

And then, a little later on,
Sad news arrived indeed:
That Jack would never hunger for,
Would never ever need,

Another glass of wine, nor yet
Another harlot's bed,
Because, in truth, Jack Falstaff
Was well and truly dead!

Meanwhile, as Henry plans for war,
And that and that alone,
He still sends envoys off to France
To claim that country's throne.

Charles the Sixth, the King of France,
Hears all they have to say.
He hears their fine words grudgingly –
But there is just no way

That he will merely step aside –
Let Henry have his realm.
He is determined and resolved
To stay right at the helm.

One envoy – Lord Exeter,
Makes Henry's feelings plain:
All France belongs to England's king –
Her hills, her dales, the Seine!

If Charles resists King Henry's claim,
Lord Exeter then said,
Then he, King Charles, must take the blame
For those who wind up dead.

'France will be responsible
For everyone who dies,
For plaintive tears of widows and
For orphans' piteous cries;

'For all the tragic loss of life,
For all the blood and gore,
For husbands, fathers, brothers,
Who'll lose their lives in war.'

The Dauphin up and boldly said,
'Let Henry do his worst,
But tell him that he'll have to fight
With me, the Dauphin, first.'

Said Exeter, 'King Henry,
Whatever else befalls,
Will make quite sure he pays you back
For sending tennis balls!'

And so the scene was thus laid out:
There'd be no more charades –
The time for talking now was through,
And war was on the cards!

The French and English Kings both found
That neither could concur,
So Henry gave the word to sail:
'We head now for Harfleur.'

And once the mighty fleet arrived
They struggled to extort
A swift and speedy victory
From France's coastal port.

But this result, King Henry found,
Was sadly not to be.
Harfleur's courageous governor
Said, 'You don't frighten me.'

He closed the town's enormous gate,
Made ready for a siege;
A courtier said to Henry,
'This could take time, my liege.'

Henry nodded wearily –
Gave orders to surround
The little port and told them all
To stay and hold their ground.

The siege went on for quite a while,
Until one fateful day
The King declared, 'I've had enough,
I'm going to have my way.'

So he approached the mighty gate,
The governor on the walls –
Then Henry called, 'Surrender now
Or take what fate befalls.

'For if you don't give up right now
It will be worse for you,
For I'll no longer guarantee
Just what my soldiers do.

'But if you open up the gate
I'll hold my soldiers back,
Your wives and children will be safe,
I'll spare them from attack.

'But if you still defy my wrath
And stubbornly persist,
If kindly acts of mercy you
Thus gracelessly resist,

'I cannot guarantee my men
Will act with due restraint
When finally we take your town –
They will not show constraint.

'Be sensible, surrender now,
Don't get my men annoyed;
And then all senseless bloodshed
We can hopefully avoid.'

The governor was not a fool,
And he was most afraid:
He knew that there was little chance
The Dauphin would send aid.

For he'd had word from France's court
They couldn't send relief,
And so the good man shouted down,
'It's now my firm belief

'I have no choice, I have to yield
Before it is too late.'
And straightaway he gave the word
To open up the gate.

And thus the siege was over then,
But what a price to pay!
For Henry's troops were tired out
And, it is true to say,

They had been very short of food –
Disease had struck some down;
No doubt they suffered heavily
When they besieged that town.

And winter was approaching –
So though the siege was won,
Disease and lack of sustenance
Had Henry on the run.

He knew he must retreat and come
To France again, next year.
He said, 'There'll be no fighting
For the present here, I fear.'

And so they set their weary way
For Calais, thus to go
Across the sea to England –
They'd not reckoned with their foe.

King Henry thought, 'It won't be long
Before the French will yield.'
But they had gathered forces up
And taken to the field.

They pushed the English eastwards
And placed their army's might
Between Henry's troops and Calais,
Thus forcing him to fight.

Henry had nowhere to hide,
He had nowhere to run,
The French outnumbered Henry's force
Something like five to one.

It all looked very dodgy,
And the odds were long indeed,
But Henry was determined
That his forces would succeed,

And beat the French into the ground.
'We'll stand and fight,' he said,
'And we won't give an inch until
Our last brave man is dead.'

And that, of course, is where they stood,
And that is where they fought,
Upon the spot that's known by all,
Right there at Agincourt!

The sight before the battle,
The night before the fray
Was something those upon the scene
Recalled to their last day.

The air is filled with whispers,
They make a humming sound,
And in the French and English camps
A hundred fires abound.

And through the soft and velvet night
As many soldiers pray,
They hear the nervous whinnying
Of horses as they neigh.

And busy hammers work right through
That long and dreadful night,
Driving rivets into steel
To seal the armour tight.

The French are very confident
The battle will be theirs,
The English – weary and worn out –
Are quite borne down with cares.

But through the ranks of Englishmen
There walks the King awhile,
He bids his men 'Good morrow',
And gives a modest smile.

He calls them, 'Brother countrymen' –
His warm way has no end –
And as he makes his cheery way
He even calls them 'Friend'.

He walks with kingly manner
And on his royal face
There shows no sign of nervousness,
No, not the slightest trace.

His kind and cheerful majesty
Gives courage to the meek,
And even cowards, when he stops,
Cease thinking things look bleak.

He sheds a warmth just like the sun,
His presence thaws cold fear,
And everyone feels bold and brave
When royal Harry's near.

And so the day of battle dawns.
Asks Gloucester, 'Where's the King?'
Bedford replies, 'He views the troops –
It is the proper thing.'

His presence thaws cold fear

'The French have sixty thousand men,'
Westmoreland glumly said.
'That's five to one,' sighed Exeter,
'And our men are half dead.'

Then King Henry joins his dukes
And hears Westmoreland say,
'Think of those not working
In England's realm today.

'If we had but a thousand here,
Fighting by our side,
We'd stand a chance of taking
All those Frenchmen for a ride.'

Calmly Henry answered him,
And with a little sigh
He said, 'Not so, dear Westmoreland,
For if we are to die,

'It's best for all in England
That those who fall right here,
Should be as few as possible,
So please be of good cheer.

'And if our fate is that we live,
Then, as we are so few,
A greater share of honour
Will thus become our due.

'Today we call St Crispin's Day –
I tell you, every year
That those who live will ever more
Regard this day as dear.

'And those who to old age survive
With pride will fondly say,
"Tomorrow is a special time
For it's St Crispin's Day."

'And they'll recount all that they did
When here upon this ground,
And as they speak their hallowed words
No-one will make a sound.

'The stories that their tongues relate
Will have a special ring
Of Bedford and Lord Westmoreland,
Of Gloucester and the King.

'Each man will teach his son this tale,
Each year to be unfurled,
And it will be recalled until
The ending of the world.

'For we, this band of brothers,
We few, we happy few,
Will always be remembered
For what we are to do.

'And every man who sheds his blood
With me upon this day,
Will always be my brother
And he can always say

'However humble was his birth –
Because he fought with me –
His actions here have earned their place
In England's history.

'And gentlemen who're now abed
In England's pleasant land
Will feel accursed they were not here
To give a helping hand.

'And when our men speak of this day
With honour and with pride,
Those absent will regret the fact
They weren't here by our side.

'They'll hold their manhoods cheaply,
As well indeed they may,
When any speaks who fought with us
Upon St Crispin's Day.'

And then the battle started,
A bloody, tangled fray,
And several times the cavalry
Of France did charge that day.

English bowmen stood behind
Stakes hammered in the ground,
And every time the French attacked
The English turned them round.

Arrows fell like hailstones on
The French troops underneath;
There didn't seem to be a spot
The French could find relief.

Arrows fell like hailstones

261

They floundered in a sea of mud
Brought on by autumn rain,
The English took advantage then
And pressed their hard-fought gain,

Till finally the French declared,
'The day is yours – you win!'
They asked if they could take their dead,
Collect their fallen kin.

There were ten thousand dead in all,
So many Frenchmen lost,
The Dauphin and the King of France
Could only count the cost.

The English army lost but few
In this great victory.
But Henry knelt in prayer and said,
'Thank God for helping me.'

He rode across the field of blood,
Across the awful mess
Of injured soldiers, dying men,
Of mayhem and distress,

Of horses crippled in the mud,
Men beaten in the fray,
Of wounded men who still would live
To fight another day.

He rode across the field of blood

The King was moved and very sad
By everything he saw,
And yet he knew this was the price
Of fighting any war.

Henry left a force in France,
Then headed for the coast,
For Calais – then to England where
He was the country's toast.

In London town, wherein he rode
In triumph through the streets,
The populace went crazy when
They heard of his great feats.

He was about as popular
As any king has been,
As loved and honoured and adored
As any monarch seen.

But in a little while the King
Returned to France again
To make a peace and to agree
That now in France he'd reign.

A meeting was at once convened –
The King of France was there,
With him his queen, and daughter too,
Sweet Katharine, so fair.

The Duke of Burgundy begins
To plead a dismal case –
He says that their beloved France
Now wears a sorry face.

'All our hedges lie untrimmed,
The grapes that make our wine
Remain neglected and unpicked;
They die upon the vine.

'Our fallow fields are in a mess,
All weeds and overgrown,
The meadows where sweet clover blew
Are left to grow un-mown.

'But this is not the only thing,
As you will soon discern:
Our children now have no desire
To study or to learn.

'War is their only study now –
They swear and wear stern looks;
They show no interest at all
In reading from their books.

'And so, King Henry, I implore,
When will this suffering cease?
Why can't you banish all this strife
And give us gentle peace?'

The King replied with measured tone,
'If peace is your desire,
I beg you then agree my terms –
That's all that I require.'

The King of France then intervened.
He said, 'Give me the chance,
To read your terms again because,
I gave them but a glance.'

As Charles and all his courtiers left,
The King said, 'If I may,
I beg your daughter, Katharine,
Remain behind and stay.'

Fair Katharine remained behind
And as they closed the doors,
King Henry said, 'How can I, Kate,
Deserve a heart like yours?'

Kate spoke but little English,
So Henry tried his best
To make her understand his love
Was real and not a jest.

Finally, she said to him
With many a nervous glance,
'Is it possible that I
Could love a foe of France?'

The King responded in a flash;
He said, 'I am no foe,
For I love France as much as you –
This I would have you know.

'I love your country far too much;
I want her to be mine.
When she is mine and I am yours
Our wishes will entwine.

'France will be yours and you'll be mine,
So will you love me, Kate?'
Poor Henry had now worked himself
Into a right old state.

'I will if my dear father
Agrees that I can wed.'
'Oh, he'll do that, without a doubt,'
King Henry boldly said.

And then the King of France returned
With Isabel, his queen,
And Burgundy and other lords
Arrived upon the scene.

Henry said with confidence,
'King Charles, upon my life,
I find that I can scarcely wait
For Kate to be my wife.'

King Charles replied in modest tone,
'If so it pleases you,
Then I don't have a problem
With what you wish to do.'

And then he said, 'I have agreed
To all the terms laid down.'
And in that moment Henry knew
He'd gained the French king's crown.

King Charles said, 'Take my daughter,
For you have truly won,
And give me children by her;
Make me happy – son.

'And let this stop all warring –
Let this now be the chance,
To bring a true alliance
Between England and fair France.'

Henry took young Katharine's hand –
For he was very keen.
He said, 'Now all bear witness –
I kiss my sovereign queen.'

And then a trumpet call rang out,
And brave King Henry said,
'France and England will be joined
When Kate and I are wed.'

⋙⋘

Sadly, Henry didn't have
Too long to be alive;
He was dead and buried by
The age of thirty-five.

He left a son, a puny child,
A helpless little thing.
He succeeded Henry as
Both France and England's king.

He became Henry the Sixth,
Theme of another play –
But that's a whole new story
To hear some other day.

He turned into a monster

270

THE WINTER'S TALE

Leontes, King of Sicily,
And Hermione, his queen,
Enjoyed a life as happy
As any ever seen.

But Leontes sometimes said,
'Although our life is sweet,
I can't deny I sometimes feel
That I would like to meet

'My dear old friend, Polixenes,
And chat with him a while,
For out of all the friends I've had,
He stood out by a mile.'

He'd often tell Hermione,
'My friend was such a brick,
To have you meet Polixenes
Would give me such a kick.'

You see, these two devoted friends
Attended the same school,
But then Leontes had returned
To Sicily to rule.

His dad had died quite suddenly
So this had put in train
A sequence of events that meant
He'd gone back home to reign.

His friend, Polixenes, as well
Had suffered a sad loss,
His father too had passed away,
So he became the boss

Of beautiful Bohemia,
Took over from his dad,
He became the country's king
Though he was still a lad.

So these two close and faithful friends
With tears in their eyes
Had fondly and reluctantly
Exchanged their last goodbyes.

Though they'd been close since childhood,
They went their separate ways,
Destined now to live apart
For their remaining days.

They sent each other letters though,
Which always gave a lift;
At Christmas and on birthdays
They always sent a gift.

And so the long years drifted by –
They never met again
Because it takes a lot of work
To rule a state and reign.

At last Polixenes gave in
To oft-repeated pleas;
The message from Leontes said:
'I'm begging on my knees.

'Please come to me in Sicily –
We'll have a great old time.
To get together once again
Would really be sublime.'

At first the visit was great fun,
For it was nothing less
Than triumph quite momentous,
A really great success.

They talked about the times they'd shared
When each had been a kid,
About the pranks and scrapes and fun
And all the things they did.

They told Hermione everything,
And she, with merry heart
Joined in their boyish happiness
And took a cheerful part

In all their conversations,
It was tremendous fun,
Until the day Polixenes
Declared the trip was done.

'I must go home,' he said at last,
'I've been away too long.'
Leontes said, 'Another month
Would surely do no wrong.'

He tried his best to make his friend
Remain a longer while.
'Alas!' Polixenes replied,
Though with a winning smile,

'I really must be going,
I should be getting back,
I've got a kingdom I must run –
And kings must not be slack.'

Hermione, with honeyed words
And her persuasive way,
Said, 'Dear Polixenes, my friend
Please linger here, I pray.

'Stay just a little longer;
We love your company.'
Enraptured, good Polixenes
Obeyed her fervent plea.

He said, 'OK, my firm resolve
You cleverly have turned.'
And though it seemed a joyous thing,
A jealousy now burned

Within Leontes' manly heart –
'Twas envy of a kind
So keen, so deep and dangerous,
It fairly turned his mind.

He thought that something was amiss:
His friend had told him, 'No!'
When he had pleaded desperately
And begged him not to go.

But one word from Hermione –
'Oh, please don't go away' –
Sufficed at once to change his mind,
And now he said he'd stay.

Although Hermione had won
Her husband's great desire,
Leontes thought each word she said
Implied she was a liar.

He also then began to think
His erstwhile loyal friend
Was after his Hermione –
This was his selfish end:

To try and take her from him...
Of course he was quite wrong,
His wife was true and faithful
To Leontes all along.

His anger and his jealousy
Both bound him in a knot
He turned into a monster –
He really lost the plot.

He sent for Lord Camillo
And told him of his pain,
He said, 'My friend is ruining
My marriage, that is plain.

'There's something dodgy going on,
I want it stopped right now.'
'Tell me your wish,' Camillo said
And gave a courtier's bow.

'Give poison to Polixenes –
I want it done today.
He's made me very angry,
I want him out the way!'

Camillo was a decent sort,
And though Leontes sounded
So certain – Lord Camillo knew
His envy was unfounded.

He knew that Queen Hermione
Was no unfaithful wife,
On this he would have gladly staked
His highly valued life.

Camillo told Polixenes
Just what the King had said,
How he desired him poisoned –
How he wished him dead.

Astounded, poor Polixenes
Was very grateful too.
He said, 'My dear Camillo
I owe great thanks to you.'

Polixenes escaped at once;
He fled away that night.
Camillo went along as well,
The pair slipped out of sight.

Once safely in Bohemia
A friendship grew between
Camillo and Polixenes,
As close as it had been

Between Leontes and the King,
Though that was in the past.
It seems that some firm friendships
Are destined not to last!

The news of their escape had put
Leontes in a rage.
He stormed about his palace –
He didn't act his age.

His fury overwhelmed him,
And he sank down into gloom.
At last he sought Hermione
Within her private room.

She was with Mamillius,
Their son, when he burst in.
He told his wife that she had lied,
Committed carnal sin.

Hermione was pregnant, but
He said, 'Your child's not mine,
The father is Polixenes.
That so-called friend's a swine!'

He raged and carried on so much
Mamillius got upset;
Leontes wasn't worried though,
He wasn't finished yet.

He just ignored his crying son
No matter how he wailed,
And turning to his wife he said,
'You're going to be jailed.'

He threw his wife in jail

279

And that is what Leontes did –
He threw his wife in jail,
And then he summoned two great lords
And told them to set sail

Towards Apollo's sacred shrine
At Delphos and, once there,
To ask the Oracle if his wife
Were having an affair.

And so the Lord Cleomenes
And good Lord Dion too
Both hastened to the Oracle
As the King had bid them do.

Meanwhile poor Hermione,
Innocent of the crime
For which she'd been imprisoned,
Was having a bad time.

She languished in the prison
Though she had done no wrong.
But then a baby girl was born:
A daughter came along.

She looked down on the lovely child,
So sweet and all brand new,
And said, 'Poor little prisoner,
I'm innocent like you.'

The Queen's best friend, Paulina,
Was visiting the jail
To see how she was feeling.
Her maid said, 'She's still frail.'

Paulina said, 'Although the King
Is acting very wild,
I still feel totally convinced
That he should see this child.'

Emilia, the maid, agreed.
'One look and we may find
The sight of such a bonny girl
Will help to change his mind.'

Paulina said, 'Then ask the Queen
If she will trust in me
And let me take the baby,
Just so the King can see

'The pretty little girl he has –
It's bound to change his view –
And he'll embrace his daughter then,
And free Hermione too.'

Emilia very soon returned
With smiles upon her face,
And in her arms she held the girl,
Wrapped in the finest lace.

She said, 'The Queen's delighted;
She thought no-one would dare
To take her daughter to the King
But bids you to beware.

'He's in an awful temper,
As I believe you know,
So pick your words most gingerly –
Be careful how you go.'

Paulina said of course she would,
Then took the baby girl.
She said, 'How could the King reject
This priceless little pearl.'

She forced her way into the King
And said, 'I do entreat
You look upon your daughter, sir.'
Then laid her at his feet.

'Have mercy on your little girl
And on your wife as well.'
But sadly all the King would do
Was stamp his feet and yell.

'Get out of here at once,' he cried.
He called Paulina's spouse.
'Antigonus, go take your wife
Out of my royal house!'

Antigonus removed his wife,
Paulina, from the room;
They left the baby with the King,
Alone to face her doom.

Paulina hoped Leontes would,
Despite his angry passion,
Become enchanted by the child
And show her some compassion.

But she was wrong for now he called,
'Antigonus, come to me!
Go, take this child and carry her
A long way out to sea.

'I do not want her presence here
For any moment more.
Find a distant, lonely place
And leave her on the shore.

'And there this child can perish;
Simply leave her there to die.'
Antigonus picked up the girl
And said, 'You can rely

'Upon your wishes being done,
My Lord. I'll do the deed.
Don't be concerned a moment more –
I'll do it with all speed.'

And when Antigonus had gone
The King arranged a trial
For much maligned Hermione.
He'd hear of no denial.

He was impatient that her guilt
Be clear for all to see.
He said, 'Word from the Oracle
Will not discourage me.

'I know my wife is guilty;
It's time that she was taught
A lesson, so with no delay
I'll bring her to the court.'

Hermione stood trembling there,
Her thoughts all in a whirl,
And she was also grieving
For her little baby girl.

Then as the trial got underway
Two men walked through the door:
'Twas Dion and Cleomenes –
This everyone now saw.

A message from the Oracle
They brought, for it had spoken.
Leontes gave stern orders,
That the seal should now be broken.

'Read what the Oracle has said,
Do so with no delay.'
The Oracle was opened up –
Here's what it had to say.

'Hermione is innocent;
Polixenes – no blame;
Camillo is a decent man;
The King now bears the name

'Of wicked tyrant, one whose words
And actions are unfair;
Leontes bears the dreadful curse
Of life without an heir

'Till that which now is lost be found,
This is my final word.'
The whole court gasped in horror
At what they had just heard.

Leontes would not heed these words,
He thought them merely lies,
Although the ancient Oracle
Was reckoned to be wise.

Then news of further tragedy
Arrived, which was the worst:
Hermione, on hearing it,
Felt that her heart would burst.

For when Mamillius had been told
'Your mother's being tried.'
The lad had felt such grief and shame
That he'd collapsed and died.

Hermione fainted on the floor
In front of all the court.
The King in desperate sorrow cried,
Now totally distraught.

He told Paulina, 'Take the Queen
And care for her, I pray.'
It was the last thing in the world
The court thought he would say.

With pity he was overcome
For his unhappy queen,
Maybe she was quite blameless;
Maybe she'd always been.

But as he thought these guilty thoughts
Paulina came and said,
'Hermione's heart has broken,
I'm afraid, my king, she's dead!'

Leontes then collapsed and cried;
His soul was torn apart.
He saw that his ill usage had
Destroyed her loving heart.

Then he recalled the Oracle –
Its words filled him with dread,
'Till that which now is lost be found,
You'll have no heir,' it said.

Now Mamillius was no more
That meant he had no heir,
Unless his daughter was brought back
And safely in his care.

But what of bold Antigonus?
Well, he'd set out to sea
With very little baggage
And the princess on his knee.

And yet this happy picture
Represents the wrong impression:
It seems to show he loved the child
He held in his possession.

But he was set upon his plan
To leave the child to die,
He'd do the deed the King required,
He would not reason why.

The ship was battered by a storm
And how the wind did roar,
Until the vessel came to land
Upon Bohemia's shore.

This was Polixenes' state,
And once the ship was safe,
Antigonus set down the child
And there he left the waif,

Alone upon the sandy shore
Where she was sure to die,
A prey to any hungry beast
That chanced to wander by.

And yet poetic justice
Was surely working there:
Antigonus, returning home,
Was eaten by a bear!

The ship was battered by a storm

289

It caught him as he made his way
Back to the waiting ship...
He really didn't stand a chance
When once it got a grip.

As for the little princess,
Well, she was quickly found,
A passing shepherd saw her
As she lay upon the ground.

She wore expensive clothes and jewels,
So it was very clear
She came of noble parentage,
But how did she get here?

The shepherd saw a message
Pinned to the baby's coat,
It was the child's name written there:
'Perdita' read the note.

He gathered up the little girl
And thus he saved her life,
And then with tender loving care
He took her to his wife.

They realised that all the jewels
Could change their life for sure;
With this new wealth they'd have no need
To struggle anymore.

He gathered up the little girl

But to conceal this treasure trove
They moved away that day
And started on another life
Some many miles away.

They bought a lot of sheep and soon
Their wealth began to grow.
They raised Perdita as their own
But never let her know

How she'd been found upon the beach,
Abandoned – all alone.
They showered her with all their love
And raised her as their own.

One noble thing the shepherd did,
One thing he firmly said:
He vowed he'd save some of the jewels
For when the girl was wed.

And so the years passed slowly by
And young Perdita grew
Into a lovely daughter –
A good girl, through and through.

Polixenes possessed a son,
One Florizel by name.
This prince was hunting one hot day –
He was in search of game.

When riding by the shepherd's hut,
He suddenly espied
A maid so fair and lovely
That it made him break his ride.

This was, of course, Perdita –
Her beauty stole his heart;
It only took a moment
And Cupid shot his dart.

Under the name of Doricles
Prince Florizel became
A frequent, ardent visitor
Disguised by this false name.

The King, his father, soon found out
Just what the lad was doing,
He wasn't pleased to find his son
Had now gone out a-wooing

A lowly shepherd's daughter,
With such a common touch,
For him to love a peasant,
This really was too much.

Polixenes called Camillo,
'You'll never guess,' he said,
'What Florizel is up to –
He must be off his head.

'He's seeing a poor shepherd girl
And spinning me some lies.
There's only one thing for it –
We must go there in disguise.

'We'll to the shepherd's dwelling
And spy on him awhile –
I find his liking for this girl
Contemptuous and vile.

'It really isn't fitting
For the offspring of a king
To lavish his affection so
On such a common thing.'

So Lord Camillo and the King
Sought out the shepherd's dwelling.
Within the King a mighty surge
Of anger was now swelling.

They approached the little hut
And as they were both nearing,
They heard a feast in progress there,
A party for sheep-shearing.

They both were made most welcome
And took a seat inside,
And when Polixenes looked round
He instantly espied

His dear, beloved Florizel.
The lad was in a chair,
Hid in a shady corner –
And the shepherd girl was there.

Polixenes approached the two
And to his son he said,
'Your mind is not on feasting,
Other thoughts are in your head.

'Your mind is on this lady,
But the pedlar's left, my boy,
And you have bought no trinkets –
You bought your love no toy.'

Florizel had no idea
That he addressed his dad;
He just surmised the old man thought
He was a lovelorn lad.

He said, 'My dearest love, right here,
Is really much too smart.
She doesn't want cheap fripperies –
She wants what's in my heart.

'And, as old man, you seem to know –
Or maybe you just guess –
What animates a lover's heart,
Please hear what I profess:

'That I will marry this dear girl,
I'll take her for my wife,
And with this solemn promise
I give myself for life.'

Polixenes went crazy then,
And ripped off his disguise.
His face was red and steaming
And anger filled his eyes.

'Young sir,' he cried with venom,
'You silly little fool!
How can you dare to speak like this?'
He really lost his cool.

'To marry such a low-born maid,
A worthless piece of tat,
A mere peasant with no class,
A scrounging shepherd's brat.

'If you see her again, I swear
Upon my dying breath,
I'll have her and her father here
Both cruelly put to death.'

This was heavy stuff indeed;
The Prince was all bereft.
The King gave orders that his son
Should follow him, then left.

Perdita there was horrified;
She thought she'd lost her beau –
For after what his dad had said
He wouldn't want to know.

But this, of course, was not the case.
The Prince refused to go
He wouldn't leave for all the world,
Because he loved her so.

But then Camillo, kind of heart,
Who thought the girl had style,
Said, 'You must both get far away
And then lie low a-while.

'I have a plan to help you both,
And this is now my thought:
The three of us will cross the sea
To Sicily's great court.

'Leontes will protect you
And keep you safe and sound,
Until Polixenes shall change
His point of view around,

'And says that he will let you wed,
And so do you agree?
Are both of you determined now
To come along with me?'

The lovers said with joy, they would –
It was the thing to do.
Camillo asked the shepherd next,
'Will you come with us too?'

The shepherd said of course he would,
And took the things he'd found
On Perdita, as she'd lain
Abandoned on the ground.

He took the baby clothes and jewels
And also took the note,
The one that had been pinned upon
Her little overcoat.

Camillo for his part was pleased
For an excuse to go,
Back to the land of Sicily
For he had missed it so.

And so they sailed for Sicily
And on arriving there
They found Leontes mourning still
Hermione and his heir.

He grieved for poor Mamillius
And it is true to tell
His wife and baby girl were both
Close to his thoughts as well.

But pleased to see Camillo back,
He grasped his hand and said,
'Oh welcome home my dear, old friend,
I feared that you were dead.'

He turned to Florizel and cried,
'You're welcome to my court.'
But when he saw Perdita there
He had the sudden thought

That she looked like Hermione.
He cried, 'You're like my queen!
I'm sure that this is just the way
My daughter would have been

'If I had not destroyed her
By actions so inept;
I've lost her now forever.'
And he broke down and wept.

Then turning to Prince Florizel
He said to the young lad,
'I miss your father's friendship –
I really miss your dad.'

But through all this Leontes
Stayed constant to one thing:
He kept his gaze on Perdita –
A very troubled king.

He told them all the story –
How he'd sent his girl away.
The shepherd thought, 'It's his *princess*
I found that fateful day.'

He showed the King the garments
And the note that he had found,
And all the other items left
Around her on the ground.

He told the King how she'd been found.
He said, 'I saw her there,
Left by a man who, afterwards,
Was eaten by a bear.'

Paulina checked the writing
In the note and then she said,
'Antigonus has written this,
So he is surely dead.'

She grieved to hear the details
Of her husband's grisly slaughter,
But despite this news, rejoiced
The King had found his daughter.

But when Leontes realised
Perdita was his child,
Great sorrow swept across him –
His feelings drove him wild.

For though he was delighted
To find his girl again,
Now thinking of Hermione
He almost went insane.

He cried, 'Oh your dear mother,
If only she were here...
I treated her appallingly,
I've done great wrong, I fear.'

Paulina then spoke up and said,
'A statue at my house,
Is the spitting image
Of Hermione, your spouse.

'It's only just been finished,
It really must be seen,
For it's the very image
Of your late lamented queen.'

The statue was quite beautiful

Leontes said he'd like to go;
Perdita too was keen
To see her mother's image
And to look upon this Queen.

They went to good Paulina's house,
Where she drew back a screen,
And there before them they all saw
A statue of the Queen.

Leontes didn't say a word,
He stood dumbstruck with awe;
He really was quite overcome
By everything he saw.

The statue was quite beautiful:
Hermione – no less.
It stood there, all resplendent
In her very finest dress.

'Is that not like your lovely queen?'
Paulina softly said.
The King replied, 'She stood like this
The day that we were wed.

'And yet she looked much younger then –
This statue makes her aged.'
Paulina said, 'The carver
With greatest skill has gauged

'How fair Hermione would look,
Were she alive today –
But let me now replace the screen
Lest your feelings make you say

'The statue is alive and breathes,
That you detect some motion,
That you persuade yourself she lives
Through your supreme devotion.'

The King cried out, 'Oh, were it true,
This surely would be bliss,
But please do not make fun of me
If now I place a kiss

'Upon this gracious monument.
Perhaps she will revive...
To me she almost seems to breathe,
She seems to be alive.'

Perdita knelt upon the floor
With long and steady gaze;
The image of her mother
Had the power to amaze.

She said, 'I could forever look
Upon my mother, dear.
I only wish I'd known her well,
Not this cold statue here.'

Paulina said, 'My gracious Lord,
If you will now approve,
And not say I have wicked powers,
I'll make the statue move.'

'Do what you will,' the King replied,
For he was quite astonished
'I shall believe it when I see,'
He quietly admonished.

Paulina ordered music,
And as it began to play,
The statue drew a heavy breath
And then began to sway.

It stepped down from the pedestal,
The most amazing thing;
Then with a smile upon its face
Embraced the startled King.

It truly *was* Hermione,
She wasn't really dead.
She prayed for blessings to come down
Upon her husband's head

And on her daughter, Perdita.
Oh, what a sight to see,
The courtiers beholding this
Were happy as could be.

Hermione had made pretence
That she had sadly died,
So when Paulina gave this news
She'd very boldly lied.

But now the Queen had been restored
Unto the King again
There's very little of our tale
That we need to explain.

Leontes and Hermione
Made Florizel their son;
They said they were most grateful
For all the Prince had done.

For he had loved their daughter
When she'd seemed of common stock;
But as they said these kindly words
They got another shock.

Polixenes himself walked in,
Looking for his boy.
When Leontes saw his friend
He almost jumped for joy.

The friends were quickly reconciled.
Polixenes agreed
That Florizel could marry –
He'd no longer have to plead.

For Perdita was nobly born
And not a 'shepherd's brat'!
So everyone lived happily
And that, at last, was that.

With no more false suspicions –
No more unhappy tears,
And all the people in this tale
Lived on for many years.

He lacks all royal charm

RICHARD THE THIRD

Our story opens gently,
Within the royal court
Of Edward, King of England,
Who's quite a decent sort.

And standing to one side of him,
Observing everything,
Is Richard, Duke of Gloucester,
Who yearns to be the King.

Edward's his oldest brother
And, though not next in line,
Richard has vowed, when Edward dies,
'The throne! I'll make it mine!'

Before he can achieve this end,
Before this longed-for day,
There are some folk he'll have to stop
From getting in his way.

But for the moment let us watch
And see him standing there,
A menacing, black spider that
Has ventured from his lair.

He's talking to himself and if
We listen for a while
We'll get a true impression
Of his most unpleasant style.

But before we hear him speak
Consider how he looks,
For he has been described this way
In many history books.

He has a threatening manner –
A sight to cause alarm,
His hair is black, his face is pale –
He lacks all royal charm.

And now he speaks and it is clear
He reeks of discontent,
He loathes himself, his dismal life,
The cards that he's been sent.

'I hate this time of peace,' he says.
'I'd rather be at war.
Spending all this time stuck here
Is really such a bore.

'I am not made for life at court
With its continual leisure,
I quite detest these wasted days,
I hate all idle pleasure.

'None of this appeals to me,'
Beneath his breath he swore.
'I'm weary of its dreariness –
I cannot stand much more.

'It doesn't suit my character –
So bleak – that when dogs see
My huddled form along the street
They bark like mad at me.

'So, as I cannot play the lover
And emulate his ways,
I'm resolved to prove a villain
In these forthcoming days.

'I intend to gain the throne
But, ere that happy day,
I must get my middle brother
Safely out the way.

'For I'm determined that the King
And Duke Clarence, this brother
Shall both of them unite in hate,
The one against the other.

'To do this, I've informed the King
Of this old prophecy:
His heirs will die by someone's hand
Whose name begins with G.

'My brother, Clarence, is called George,
With luck the King will think
That he's a mortal enemy
And throw him in the clink.

'But here comes brother Clarence now,
With such a scowling face!
Greetings, brother – why this guard
That waits upon your Grace?'

Clarence smiled to see him there,
He thought he was his friend,
Little did he realise
That Richard sought his end.

'The King hears prophecies,' he said,
'Heeds old wives' tales, it seems,
That say his heirs will all be killed –
He sees this in his dreams.

'The murderer's name begins with G,
And so within the hour
Of hearing this he made his plans
To throw me in the Tower.'

'Alack, my Lord,' dark Richard said,
'I know you're not to blame.
It's just your sad misfortune that
George is your Christian name.

'But fear not, I'll to the King,
Where I will plead for you.
I find this most peculiar and
It's most distressing too.'

Clarence thanked his brother
But as he went away,
Richard, with a selfish sneer,
Had other words to say.

'Go, tread the path, my brother,
From which you'll not return,
You're simple, plain and trusting,
For you will never learn

'That I love you so very much
That I will send your soul,
To Heaven as a special gift:
Your death is now my goal.'

With Clarence in the Tower
One hurdle was removed
In Richard's path towards the crown;
His chances were improved.

He now set out to win a wife,
But what a devilish plan!
The woman that he wished to wed
Was lovely Lady Anne.

Richard had killed her husband
And the husband's dad as well,
So she thought Richard Gloucester
Had earned his place in hell.

Her husband's father once was King –
Henry the Sixth he'd been –
And so we enter now upon
A quite amazing scene.

Despite these two foul murders
Still Richard sought a way
To marry lovely Lady Anne
And he'd brook no delay.

For she was well connected,
Her hand would help him get
The throne of England for himself,
And so he cast his net.

He found her with a coffin,
Her emotions deep and raw
For it contained the last remains
Of her dear father-in-law.

He found her with a coffin

As she walked along she sobbed,
Her tears came in a flood –
'Cursed be the hand that made these holes
And spilt this precious blood.'

She cursed Richard of Gloucester,
She cursed his hated name,
She left no-one in any doubt
Of where she laid the blame.

Then from the shadows there appeared
A fiend in human form,
The sight of which made Lady Anne
Rage furiously and storm.

For it was Richard Gloucester
That she saw standing there.
She cried, 'How could you come here now,
How could you even dare?'

Richard addressed the bearers,
His face a solemn frown:
'You that bear the King,' he said,
'I bid you lay him down.'

'Oh, black magician!' Anne cried out.
'Don't stop our worthy deed,
Not when it was your filthy hand
That made poor Henry bleed.'

'Set down the coffin,' Richard cried,
'And do not question why,
Or all you bearers here this morn
Will with King Henry lie.'

The coffin was set down in haste.
Then Anne began to yell –
She really let him have it,
She really gave him hell.

But Richard just deflected
Her every single word;
He took her accusations
As though they'd not occurred.

He simply paid her compliments,
And so her anger boiled;
The more he uttered honeyed words
The more that she recoiled.

He finally admitted,
'Your husband and the King,
I killed them both – and, yes, I know
It was an evil thing.

'But I reply, I did it –
Committed this high treason –
Merely out of love for you...
This was my only reason.'

She cried, 'You killed my husband!'
He said, 'To make you free!
To find a better husband –
And that better man is me.'

She spat upon him saying,
As the spit flew in his face,
'I wish that it were poison.'
He said, 'From such a place

'Poison would be, oh, so sweet.'
She cried amid her sighs,
'Get from my sight, you loathsome toad,
For you infect my eyes.'

She said she hated him so much,
Entirely and above
Anyone she'd ever known–
Still he professed his love.

Then Richard, laying bare his chest,
Exclaimed, 'Avenge your Lord,
Likewise the monarch whom I killed.'
Then handed her his sword.

'Don't hesitate,' he cried. 'I killed
King Henry – yes it's true.
I also killed your husband,
Spurred by my love for you.'

'Though I wish your death,' she said,
'I cannot kill you here.'
'Then bid me kill myself,' he cried.
'I'll do it, have no fear.'

'No, no! Put up your sword,' she groaned.
He said, 'As I'm to live,
Take this my ring, in fair exchange
For love you soon will give.'

The Lady Anne took up his ring
And then went on her way.
When she had gone he praised himself –
As well indeed he may.

'Was ever woman won this way?
Was ever woman wooed?
Did ever man attempt to win
A woman in this mood?

'She has now forgiven me
In spite of my great wrong,
So I will have her now for sure –
But I'll not keep her long!'

But what about poor Clarence?
What has become of him,
Imprisoned in the Tower
On a monarch's fickle whim?

He's going to get two callers
Who steal there in the night,
And sadly poor old Clarence
Will get a dreadful fright.

They carry a death warrant
Initialled by the King.
It's all a bit unfair because
He hasn't done a thing.

But having signed this warrant
For the brother once held dear,
(And truly it was based upon
A quite unfounded fear)

The King had changed his mind and so
He'd quickly sent another
To tell the keeper of the Tower
Not to kill his brother.

But it will come as no surprise
That Richard – foul and mean –
Had stopped the second message,
Found a way to intervene.

And so the murderers approached
Duke Clarence in his cell,
They were dressed in black and looked
Like evil ghouls from hell.

Clarence realised at once
What they had come there for.
He pleaded for his life and said,
'I did not break the law.

'I love the King, my brother.
Why does he want me dead?
I've never been disloyal.
I care for him,' he said.

'Send for my brother, Gloucester.
Please put away your knife.
He will reward you handsomely
If you will spare my life.'

What irony that Clarence thought
Richard would intervene!
It was as fruitless a desire
As there has ever been.

One murderer then cried aloud,
'Look to your back, my Lord.'
The other said, 'Take that!' And then
He stabbed him with his sword.

'To make quite sure he's dead,' he said,
'This stabbing I'll combine
With drowning in the butt within
That's filled with malmsey-wine.'

The other murderer recoiled.
He cried, 'O bloody deed!
How savagely he's been dispatched,
How sad to see him bleed!

'I wish that I could wash my hands
Of this foul act I've seen.'
His partner said, 'Gloucester shall know
How tardy you have been.'

The first replied, 'Here take my fee –
Tell Gloucester what I say.
For I repent the Duke is slain
And now I shall away.

'For this foul deed will out when once
It's known the Duke is dead.
I only wished I'd taken steps
To save the Duke,' he said.

322

'To make quite sure he's dead,' he said

King Edward was distraught when told
That Clarence had been killed.
He saw his first instruction
Had most sadly been fulfilled.

He had no way of knowing that
Richard had intervened.
The King declared he'd loved the Duke
Since Clarence first was weaned.

He cried, 'The order was reversed,
So how is Clarence dead?'
'He died by your first order,'
Wily Richard slyly said.

The King then left and Richard had
The brazen gall to say,
'Clarence will be avenged, by God,
Upon some future day.'

What a two-faced dog he was!
A villain, to be sure –
But wait a while, for it gets worse...
Oh yes, there's so much more.

For now we look upon a scene
As sad as any known,
As Clarence's two children grieve
At being left alone.

They are being counselled
With sympathetic talk,
By their kindly grand-mama,
The good Duchess of York.

And then the Queen, King Edward's wife,
Her hair a tangled mess,
Comes rushing to the chamber
In evident distress,

'What's up?' the Duchess asked the Queen.
The Queen just beat her head.
'Edward, my Lord, your son, our King,
Has passed away,' she said.

'What will become of all of us?
How will the branches grow?
When now the root that was the King
Is laid so very low.'

She cried great tears of sorrow
But Earl Rivers who was there
Said, 'Get a grip upon yourself –
There's danger to beware.

'The King is dead and though we grieve
You *must* act right away:
Summon your son Prince Edward now –
Oh, bring him here, I pray.

'Let him be crowned without delay,
While in control and able,
Do it now with all good haste
To keep the kingdom stable.

'For in your son your safety dwells,
In young Prince Edward's throne;
In dead King Edward's grave there lies
Sorrow – and that alone.'

But then a brooding presence came
Into the mourning room,
Upon a scene of deep despair
He shed a further gloom.

For there stood Richard Gloucester,
A dark and huddled form,
Crouching, whilst suppressing
An inward raging storm.

He approached the Queen and said,
'We all of us have cause
To mourn our dear, lost, shining star...
But, Madam, prithee pause.

'All the crying in the world
Can give but small relief;
However much you wail and moan
It will not ease your grief.'

He slowly moved around the room,
Exuding sympathy.
He said, 'My brother's sudden loss
Is such a blow to me.'

It was of course an empty show;
He played the fawning lamb.
His motives though were insincere,
An ostentatious sham.

They all agreed the youthful prince,
Without undue delay,
Should soon be brought to London –
Indeed, come right away.

This matter settled, they all left,
But Richard stayed alone –
Save for the Duke of Buckingham,
The only friend he's known.

Buckingham told Richard,
'Now to avoid the worst
We must make sure we reach the prince
And his young brother first.'

Richard whispered quietly,
'It's time to throw the dice
To win the throne of England,
So I'll act on your advice.'

The princes came to London,
An anxious, worried pair.
They found their Uncle Richard
Was waiting for them there.

Prince Edward asked his uncle,
'Where is the Queen, my mother,
And what do you intend to do
With me and my dear brother?'

'You will be cared for,' Richard said,
'You'll stay within the Tower,
And there you will be housed until
Your coronation hour.'

Prince Edward looked most troubled,
A frown upon his face.
'I do not like the Tower,' he said.
'I really hate the place.'

Then his brother, Duke of York,
Spoke up and said, 'Oh dear!
The Tower is such an awful place –
There's so much there to fear.

'For I've been told, in dead of night
The corridors play host
To angry fiends they say include
Our Uncle Clarence's ghost.'

Prince Edward then said bravely,
'I fear no uncle dead.'
'Nor none that lives, I trust, young sir,'
His Uncle Richard said.

The prince replied, 'I hope not too,
But let us now depart
Unto the Tower, where I go
With very heavy heart.'

Once the princes were within
The Tower, out the way,
Richard spoke to Buckingham;
He had these words to say:

'We must arouse the populace,
We must do everything
To make them feel quite happy
About my being king.

'You must address the rabble,
And to them all proclaim
The princes aren't of royal blood;
They have no rightful claim.

'You must declare them bastards – say
Their father, the late king,
Was no true monarch; that he lied
About just everything.'

So Buckingham addressed the crowd
Who gathered there to hear –
But they all stood in silence,
And no-one raised a cheer.

He spoke about the princes,
Tried deftly to defame
Their honoured reputation
And blacken their good name.

He said, 'They're illegitimate,
They cannot claim the crown.'
He did most everything he could
To put the princes down.

He cried, 'Richard of Gloucester!
Now he's the man to reign.'
The crowd just stood in silence,
So he yelled it out again.

He cried, 'God save King Richard!
No-one else will do.'
But getting such a poor response
He silently withdrew.

Richard was beside himself
On hearing how the crowd
Had sullenly rejected him;
He cursed them all out loud.

Buckingham then calmed him down,
He quietened his tirade.
He said, 'My Lord, it's time to act
Like a reluctant maid.'

He outlined then his devious plan,
Which made sly Richard smile.
The scheme appealed for it was honed
With cunning, care and guile.

Buckingham went before the crowd,
Then summoned Richard there.
But a message came straight back:
He was at fervent prayer.

'Richard's not King Edward,'
The pious message said.
'He doesn't waste his precious time
In a lascivious bed.

'He kneels in meditation,
His soul of one accord
With holy hermits everywhere –
He's praying to the Lord.'

Another message then was sent
Again the answer came –
And, no surprise, its contents were
In every way the same.

And so he tried a final time;
He sent another word.
What happened at this third attempt
Was really quite absurd.

Upon a balcony above
Came Richard, book in hand,
A bishop either side of him
Who each looked rather grand.

Buckingham called out aloud,
He begged him to come down
And greet the people waiting there
And to accept the crown.

Richard listened to his pleas
But kept on saying, 'No.
I am not worthy to be King,
And this you surely know.'

But gradually he came around.
He said, 'Since you all ask,
I will accept reluctantly
This very daunting task.

'I am not worthy to be King'

'It is a heavy burden
That you buckle to my back,
But I will suffer this great load
And never ever slack.'

And so with protestations
This two-faced, cunning thing
Allowed the crowd assembled there
To choose him for their King.

Cried Buckingham, 'Long live the King,
The crown we'll now bestow.'
Dissembling, Richard answered,
'Well it seems you'll have it so.'

And to the bishops he then said,
'Before I start my reign
Let us return with haste unto
Our holy prayers again.'

And so they crowned him England's King;
Anne, now his wife, made Queen
In splendid pageant quite as fine
As any ever seen.

So everything he had desired
Had finally occurred,
For now he sat upon the throne,
King Richard, England's third.

Once King he spoke to Buckingham
And said, 'I wish to thrive,
But this is very difficult
While Edward is alive.'

Buckingham did not perceive
The plan in Richard's head.
'Let me be plain,' the King cried out.
'I want the princes dead.'

Richard saw that Buckingham
Did not approve the thought
Of yet another bloody deed
At this, the royal court.

So in that moment Richard turned
On Buckingham, his friend.
He thought, 'His days advising me
Are coming to an end.'

But Richard was determined
That the princes now should die,
He summoned Sir James Tyrrel
And asked him with a sigh,

'Would you kill a friend of mine?'
Said Tyrrel, 'This I'd do,
And yet in truth I'd rather kill
Two enemies for you.'

Richard said, 'These enemies
Disturb each waking hour –
Tyrrel, I mean those princes who
Are locked up in the Tower.'

'Give me the means to reach them,'
Tyrrel said, 'And then for sure,
I will dispatch them right away;
They'll trouble you no more.'

And then within an hour or two,
When dim had grown the light,
Tyrrel sent two men to kill
The boys that very night.

They crept into the princes' cell
Like wolves who stalk a hare,
And then with murderous villainy
They smothered them both there.

Once the deed was carried out –
Killed foully as they slept –
The evil bloody murderers
Were so upset, they wept.

One said, 'They lay like gentle babes,
A prayer book at their side;
It is no wonder that we both
Have broken down and cried.'

But, cry or not, the deed was done.
Came Tyrrel to the King –
Richard, when he saw him, asked,
'Is it good news you bring?'

'They both are slain,' Tyrrel replied.
The King asked, 'Sure they're dead?'
'I saw the pair of them, my Lord –
And buried too,' he said.

They crept into the princes' cell

King Richard with these murders done,
Was not quite finished yet.
He now desired to change his wife –
And his resolve was set.

He did away with poor Queen Anne.
Buckingham also fled.
The King no longer favoured him;
He feared now for his head.

For Buckingham had asked the King
To give him a reward:
'For helping you to gain the throne,
For risking all, my Lord.'

But Richard was ungrateful –
He had these words to say:
'I'm not in giving mood right now,
Don't feel that way today.'

Buckingham had seen at once
Things didn't look too good,
So he had fled and gone away,
As far off as he could.

And these events began the end
For Richard, called the Third,
As news began to spread abroad
Of all that had occurred.

And Buckingham now raised a force
To fight his erstwhile friend;
And many forces now conspired
To bring about his end.

For Henry, Earl of Richmond,
Had just then by happy chance
Landed with his army –
He'd come across from France.

So both these mighty armies
Combined with just one aim:
To rid the world of Richard –
Their purpose was the same.

But a little while before
The battle would be fought,
Poor, unhappy Buckingham
Most tragically got caught.

He was shown no mercy,
For Richard wished him dead,
So he was executed
By chopping off his head.

'A horse! A horse! My kingdom
For a horse!' he wildly yelled

A mighty battle now commenced
Upon fair Bosworth field,
Each side determined that they'd win –
And neither one would yield.

The battle raged throughout the day,
The scene a field of blood,
Yet they fought on ferociously,
Upon a sea of mud.

Then in the midst of battle
Richard lost his trusty steed,
This is the moment that we hear
The desperate monarch plead:

'A horse! A horse! My kingdom
For a horse!' he wildly yelled.
He knew that standing there on foot
He could be quickly felled.

The Earl of Richmond saw him
And there began a fight,
A test of courage, strength and will,
A truly stirring sight.

Their swords both clashed together
In a really frightful fray,
Until the moment Richard fell –
Richmond had won the day.

'And this belongs to you, my Lord'

342

With Richard dead upon the ground
The Earl then raised his head.
'The day is ours,' he cried aloud.
'The wicked dog is dead.'

And then the good Earl Stanley
Took the crown from Richard's head,
'And this belongs to you, my Lord,'
To Richmond he then said.

They crowned him then, King Henry,
The Seventh he became,
The first of all the Tudors
Who for England gained great fame.

He said, 'This realm of England
Has wept a stream of blood,
Brought on it by an evil King,
A grim torrential flood.

'But now we say it's over –
The tyrant now is slain,
Let fair and prosperous days begin,
Let peace reign here again.'

Valentine would raise his eyes
Unto the heavens above

THE TWO GENTLEMEN OF VERONA

A long time in the distant past
You may say 'way back when',
There lived in fair Verona
Two noble gentlemen.

The first one was called Valentine,
And Proteus, the other;
Their friendship was so close and true
Each felt he had a brother.

Now Proteus loved a lady,
And Julia was her name.
Everyone in town agreed
She was a cracking dame.

Proteus would speak of love,
'It's great,' he'd say, 'oh my!'
But on this subject these two friends
Could not see eye to eye.

For Valentine had no-one
So when Proteus spoke of love
Valentine would raise his eyes
Unto the heavens above.

The more that Proteus spoke about
Fair Julia, his passion,
The more that Valentine would tease
For speaking in this fashion.

He said, 'My freedom's best by far
Than tortured love, my friend.
Your lovelorn life appears to cause
You heartache without end.'

Then Valentine one day spoke out:
'Milan's the place,' he said.
'I've had Verona up to here;
This town is really dead.

'For if a young man stays at home,
I'm certain that he'll find
He'll end up quite dull-witted
And with a narrow mind.

'If you did not love Julia
In the desperate way you do,
I'd ask you to accompany me –
It would be good for you.

'But stay and may love thrive for you
Each and every day.'
'Farewell, my friend,' said Proteus.
'I'll miss you while away.'

Valentine left for Milan –
When he was out of sight,
Proteus took up pen and ink
And he began to write.

He wrote to fairest Julia,
To advocate his suit;
He hoped that in her heart sweet thoughts
Of love would soon take root.

For though she loved him deeply,
With a love that was as true
As his for her, she'd never said
The words: 'I love you too'.

She was a noble lady
And thought it for the best
To keep the hand of cards she held
Concealed, close to her chest.

So Proteus wrote his letter
With hopes he would persuade
The lady to return his love,
Then gave it to her maid.

She took it to her mistress but
She gave the note no heed.
She said, 'It's not the kind of thing
I'd ever want to read.'

She told the maid, Lucetta, 'Go –
And take the letter too.'
But really it was not the thing
She wanted her to do.

She didn't want her maid to know
She'd felt sweet Cupid's dart
And that the handsome Proteus
Had stolen her poor heart.

And yet she wished to read the note,
So called her maid once more.
Lucetta came into the room
As she had done before.

'Now what's the time?' asked Julia.
Her maid thought, 'There's no way
My mistress really cares at all
About the time of day.'

She offered her the letter,
But Julia lost her cool;
She said she didn't want a note
From some poor, love-sick fool.

She said, 'Don't you presume to guess
What my true wishes are.
You are a very cheeky maid –
Too impudent by far.'

She grabbed the letter, crumpling it,
And making lots of creases,
And then she tore the paper up
In tiny little pieces.

And as Lucetta made her way
Towards the chamber door
So Julia took the fragments up
And threw them on the floor.

Lucetta went to pick them up
And sighed a passive sigh,
But Julia said, 'Get out of here,
Just let the paper lie.'

Once Lucetta had retired
Her mistress felt much better,
For now she was completely free
To gather up the letter.

On studying the fragments
The words that first she read,
Were these: 'Love wounded Proteus.'
'Oh, bless his heart,' she said.

Lamenting all his loving words
She'd thrown upon the floor
She wrote a kinder letter
Than any sent before.

When Proteus received it
He truly was delighted,
For here was indication that
His love might be requited.

'Oh, lovely Julia!' he exclaimed.
'To think you really care...'
But then his father came along.
He said, 'What have you there?'

'It is from Valentine,' he lied.
'Let's see,' his father said.
'Come, let me read his latest news.'
But Proteus shook his head.

'He hasn't much to say,' he sighed,
'Though he's a lucky man,
For he has been befriended
By the grand Duke of Milan.

'He says how much he wishes
I was in Milan as well.
It all sounds so exciting
From what he has to tell.'

His father said, 'Would you not like
To go there and to spend
Some time at that distinguished court
And be there with your friend?'

'My duty lies,' said Proteus,
Trying his best to hide
The true emotions that he felt –
'To be here at your side.'

His father had been chatting
To a friend who'd said to him,
'Why do you let your son stay here
Indulging every whim?

'For most young men go travelling,
They venture far and wide;
It's very strange that Proteus
Remains here by your side.

'And look! His good friend Valentine
Is at Milan's great court –
Just think of all the benefits
And lessons he'll be taught.

'I am surprised that you allow
Your son to wallow here,
For it will do him little good,
And ruin him I fear.'

So now, whilst speaking to his son
The friends' wise words came back,
He felt that it had surely been
A timely little chat.

He said, 'You say that Valentine
Would like you in Milan...
I think he's right – it would transform
A boy into a man.

'With your good friend I quite agree,
So to Milan you'll go.'
Proteus saw immediately
That he could not say 'No'.

His father always got his way.
He sighed an earnest sigh;
He blamed himself for this result
Because he'd told a lie.

He'd been untruthful to his dad,
So now he must depart
And leave the maiden there behind
Who'd stolen his poor heart.

When Julia heard the awful news
Her calm flew out the door;
She soon stopped playing hard to get
And very quickly swore

Her everlasting love for him,
And then both vowed those things
That every lover promises –
They then exchanged gold rings.

Proteus then left for Milan
And on arriving there
He found that his friend Valentine
Was now the one to care.

He'd fallen for fair Silvia,
She loved him madly too;
But it was all a secret,
So no-one else there knew.

She was the Duke's own daughter,
The centre of his life,
But he was quite determined
She'd be someone else's wife.

To Valentine the Duke had shown
Great friendship from the start,
But he would not allow the lad
To claim his daughter's heart.

For he had quite made up his mind
She'd marry Thurio,
And Valentine would never do,
Although she loved him so.

But Silvia hated Thurio,
Despite his ardent pleas,
For he had none of Valentine's
Appealing qualities.

*For he had none of Valentine's
Appealing qualities*

The day that Proteus arrived
Valentine was engaged
In making fun of Thurio
And getting him enraged.

And they were both with Silvia
When the Duke came in to say,
'Behold, your good friend Proteus
Has turned up here today.'

Valentine was overjoyed.
He said, 'My Lord, his face
Has such an air of nobleness,
His manner has such grace.'

'Then welcome him,' the Duke replied.
'He's come here seeking you.
Now greet your good friend Proteus –
And with no more ado.'

Proteus strode into the room,
All bluster and good cheer;
Valentine said happily,
'It's good to see you here.'

He turned to Silvia and said,
'Meet Proteus, sweet dove.'
And Proteus, on meeting her,
Fell instantly in love.

When later they left Silvia
A laughing Proteus said,
'So tell me how you're now in love,
Whatever turned your head?'

Said Valentine, 'I must admit,
I'm now of your accord,
For love has won and humbled me –
He is a mighty Lord.'

Proteus laughed to hear his friend
Admit this change of view,
But he was an unworthy friend
In what he planned to do.

He thought, 'I am determined now
To make fair Silvia mine.'
He would throw over Julia, and
Betray good Valentine.

Then Valentine explained to him
And trustingly revealed
How that the Duke was in the dark
And how they had concealed

The passion that they truly shared –
How it was only known
To Silvia and to himself,
The two of them alone.

'The Duke won't let her marry me,'
He said with great remorse.
'He is resolved – his heart is set
To take a different course.

'The Duke intends that Silvia
Shall marry Thurio,
So we are planning to elope –
But no-one else must know.

'Tonight when everyone's retired
And safe and sound in bed,
Sweet Silvia and I will steal
To Mantua,' he said.

He showed his friend a ladder;
It was made from strongest rope:
'This will be the vehicle
By which we will elope.

'She'll hang it from her window
Upon this very night,
And once she's climbed down safely
We'll disappear from sight.'

It's hard to credit such a thing
But in that hour, forsooth,
Proteus thought he'd go and tell
Fair Silvia's dad the truth.

So he sought out the worthy Duke –
Engaged him in a chat;
And after idle banter ... well,
He slyly told him that

He felt he should inform him
Of some news that he had heard.
He told him of the lovers' plan –
Repeated every word.

He said, 'Though I betray a friend
I really can't conceal
What Valentine is planning,
And I feel I must reveal

'His scheme to steal your daughter,
For you've been kind to me;
I feel it is my duty –
I just can't let things be.'

He told him, 'Valentine's become
A very cunning bloke,
For he's concealed a ladder
Beneath his very cloak.'

The Duke then said to Proteus,
'If this is all the truth,
Then you're a most upstanding man,
A decent, honest youth.'

'*For he's concealed a ladder*
Beneath his very cloak'

So when the Duke saw Valentine
All wrapped up in his cloak –
Concealing his rope ladder –
The Duke to him thus spoke:

'Where are you rushing to, good sir,
At such a frantic pace?'
Sly Valentine then stopped and said,
'Excuse me please, your Grace...

'I have some letters to deliver.'
This was of course untrue.
The Duke said, 'They can wait awhile,
I would have words with you.

'Please tarry for a moment,
And put aside your mail.'
Then he began an artful ruse,
By telling him this tale.

He said, 'I have decided that
I must disown my child,
For she's become unruly,
Disrespectful, brash and wild.

'She will not marry Thurio
Although this is my wish,
So I will serve my Silvia up
A most unwelcome dish.

'From here on in, she's on her own,
I'll make her leave my house –
Her beauty and her grace alone
Must gain for her a spouse.

'Once this is done, I do intend
To find myself a wife –
In fact I've found a lovely lass
With whom to share my life.

'But I'm right out of practice;
I don't know how to woo.
So I was hoping that you'd help
And tell me what to do.'

So Valentine then gave advice
On what to do to court;
He gave the Duke in detail
All the knowledge that he sought.

'But there is still a problem,'
The Duke went on. 'You see,
Her father keeps her guarded
And she's under lock and key.

'I cannot get to see her –
There really is no way
That I can get to visit her
At any time of day.'

'Then go at night,' said Valentine.
'Be sure to take with you,
Some rope so you can scale the wall –
That's just the thing to do.

'And on your way conceal the rope
Beneath a cloak like mine,
And you will see that everything
Will all turn out just fine.'

'Oh, let me borrow your fine cloak,'
The Duke then up and cried.
He grabbed at Valentine's great cloak
And threw it open wide.

And there he saw the ladder,
'So, what's all this?' he said.
And in the cloak he saw a note
From Silvia, which read:

'My Valentine, I'll wait for you
Upon this very night.'
On reading this the troubled Duke
Turned pale – he went quite white.

He angrily told Valentine
How base and false he'd been.
He said, 'To steal my daughter thus
Would be extremely mean.'

He banished Valentine from court.
He said, 'I'll make it plain –
Don't ever try to see or speak
To Silvia again.'

So Valentine was forced to leave
Milan – where could he go?
He knew if he went home, his dad
Just wouldn't want to know.

While he was wandering through a wood
A mile outside Milan,
About as low as he could get,
A lonely, banished man,

Some robbers jumped upon him.
They said, 'Your cash, my lad.'
He told them that the clothes he wore
Were truly all he had.

He said, 'I'm but a banished man;
My whole life's in a mess.'
They quickly saw he told the truth
From his immense distress.

And they could also tell at once
From his most noble air
That he was just the answer
To a humble robber's prayer.

They said, 'We need a leader.
There's a post here to be filled –
And if you don't accept the job,
We're sorry, you'll be killed.'

Valentine no longer cared
What could become of him,
And so he thought he might as well
Indulge the robbers' whim.

So noble Valentine, who'd been
So well behaved and good,
Became the outlaws' leader,
Just like England's Robin Hood.

But meanwhile, what of Julia?
Well, she was wont to cry
Because her darling Proteus
No longer dwelt close by.

So she resolved to seek him out
By going to Milan,
And on the road, for safety's sake,
She'd dress up as a man.

They said, 'We need a leader'

Her maid, Lucetta, went as well,
Dressed in the selfsame way,
And when they reached Milan they found
An inn in which to stay.

The landlord spoke to Julia
And, with a pleasant smile,
Said, 'Would you like to come and hear
Some music for a while?

'The music has been organised
By one young man tonight
To serenade a lady fair –
It should be quite a sight.'

Alas! A frown crossed Julia's face.
The reason was, you see,
She thought, 'If I meet Proteus
He'll be upset with me.

'He'll think I am no lady;
He'll think I'm much too bold –
My coming to Milan for him
Will turn his passion cold.'

But still she said she'd go along
To hear the serenade,
So hurried off with her new host
And with her faithful maid.

They to the ducal palace went,
And, walking through the door,
Proteus declaiming love
Was what the trio saw.

He vowed he loved sweet Silvia,
But Julia heard her say
He was a naughty fellow
For speaking in this way.

'What of your true love, Julia?'
Fair Silvia said with passion,
'And how could you treat Valentine
In this disloyal fashion?'

She slammed her window on him,
She said she'd hear no more;
His base, unfaithful conduct
Really shook her to the core.

For she still loved young Valentine –
Her love just knew no end –
How could sly Proteus act like this
Towards his once good friend?

And Julia was most upset –
She flew into a rage.
Then she contrived that she'd become
Her faithless lover's page.

And this was all made easy
On account of Julia's ploy
Of dressing up, to make herself
Look like a handsome boy.

Proteus offered her a job,
Commanding, 'Do one thing,
Go now to Silvia for me
And give her this gold ring.'

She saw it was the self-same ring
She gave him when he left!
This action now made Julia
Feel totally bereft.

But when she went to Silvia
She was most relieved to find
The lady that her Proteus loved
Was really very kind.

Fair Silvia said, 'I do not want
Proteus or his love,
For he once told me he adored
His Julia way above

'All other women in the world.
He now discards her – so
He's really not the type of man
That I would want to know.'

Julia said, 'I'm pleased to find
Your actions are so true...
I feel I should reveal the fact
That I know Julia too.'

She then spoke highly of herself –
As you'd expect she would.
She said, 'This Julia is fair,
Respected, sweet and good.

'She's just about as pretty
As one's eyes could ever see,
And truthfully I must admit
She looks a bit like me.'

Then Julia offered her the ring,
And Silvia cried, 'The cur!
That's Julia's ring – for he once said
That it belonged to her.'

And so fair Silvia's kindliness
Began to make a start
To cure poor Julia's sadness,
And ease her broken heart.

Silvia still loved Valentine –
This I think we know –
So she was quite determined
Not to marry Thurio.

Now she decided she would go
To Mantua – she'd heard
That Valentine was hiding there –
At least that was the word.

But he was with the robbers
And he'd now inspired a fashion
For thieves to treat their victims
With some kindness and compassion.

Silvia left for Mantua,
And Eglamour went too –
An old man to protect her,
But, in truth, what could he do?

For when a robber stopped them
As they traversed the wood
Eglamour just ran away –
So *he* was not much good.

The robber saw that Silvia
Was truly terrified:
She shook with fear from head to toe,
Her eyes stared open wide.

Eglamour just ran away

'Be not afraid,' he gently said –
So Silvia felt relief –
'For I will take you now to meet
My wise, fair-minded chief.'

But then her fear returned with force.
She thought, 'Oh dear! Poor me!
Valentine – my dearest love –
I suffer this for thee.'

But as the robber took her
To meet his chief close by,
Fair Silvia caught a movement
With her sharp-sighted eye.

It was unfaithful Proteus
With Julia at his side,
Still in the costume of a page,
Her own true self to hide.

For he had followed Silvia
And now, without delay,
Proteus fought the robber off
And sent him on his way.

And now he'd saved fair Silvia –
Given the thief the boot –
Proteus once more set out
To press his lover's suit.

Julia stood there silently
As Proteus urged his case.
She wore a solemn, anxious look
Upon her woeful face.

She thought that this courageous act
Of saving Silvia's life,
Would mean, for sure, that Proteus gained
Fair Silvia for his wife.

But as she stood there watching these
Events she so much feared,
Silvia's true love, Valentine,
Quite suddenly appeared.

Appraised of Silvia's capture
And all that had occurred,
He'd come at once with every haste
To check on what he'd heard.

And there he found sly Proteus,
His erstwhile faithful friend,
Declaring love for Silvia
He vowed would have no end.

Then Proteus saw Valentine
And, seized with great remorse,
Apologised that he had let
His actions take this course.

Valentine was very kind –
To such a great degree
That he informed his selfish friend:
'I shall set Silvia free.

'All my loving interest
I gladly give to you.'
It was a quite astounding thing
For Valentine to do.

But Julia on hearing this
Could not believe her ears,
For it confirmed the very worst
Of all her girlish fears.

Thinking Proteus would accept
She fainted on the ground...
But after a few moments
She started coming round.

Proteus eyed her closely.
'Well, bless my soul!' he said.
'It is my lovely Julia,
Unless I'm off my head.'

He saw her love for him still burned –
It was extremely plain;
And this – her care and constancy –
Brought *his* love back again.

He dropped upon one knee and begged,
'Let's make a brand new start.'
She said, 'Oh yes, my Proteus,
With all my loving heart.'

So now that they were reconciled
Good Valentine then swore,
Eternal love for Silvia
And said, 'Be mine, once more.'

But at the very moment
When true love had won the day,
The Duke and silly Thurio
Came passing by that way.

Thurio grabbed Silvia,
'This maid is mine,' he said.
Valentine replied, 'Stand back,
Or you will end up dead.

'If you so much as touch her
You will breathe your final breath.
If you don't heed my words, right now,
I'll bring about your death.'

Thurio was a coward.
He said, 'I'll tell you what:
Only a fool would fight a duel
For one who loves him not.'

The Duke then said to Thurio,
'The fact that you won't fight
Shows me you're not a man at all,
So get out of my sight.

'I applaud you, Valentine.
You've proved to God above,
And also to myself, that you
Deserve my daughter's love.'

Valentine then thanked the Duke
And gravely kissed his hand,
And then he asked for clemency
Towards his robber band.

He said that really, by and large,
Their crimes were very small,
The Duke replied he'd pardon them,
The whole band, one and all.

Then Proteus was forced to tell
Exactly how he'd been
As false a friend as anyone
Had really ever seen.

But once he had apologised,
(A task he found quite tough)
It was agreed by everyone
That he had done enough.

So to Milan they all returned
And there the good Duke said,
'We'll have a celebration
And you can all get wed.'

So with this happy outcome
Our little intrigue ends;
Verona's two young gentlemen
Once more became best friends.

His doctors all just scratch their heads

ALL'S WELL THAT ENDS WELL

We start when old Count Roussillon
Has drawn his final breath;
His son and heir now takes his place
Upon the old man's death.

The King of France, he loved the Count
And when he heard he'd died,
He called the young son, Bertram,
To join him at his side.

He wished to pass his favour
From the old Count to the new,
What a really gracious thing
For such a King to do!

Of course this regal summons
With which Bertram had been blest,
Amounted to an order,
It was no polite request.

He had no choice but to attend,
He had to leave that day;
No-one with an ounce of sense
Would choose to disobey.

His loving mum, the Countess,
Was tortured by the thought
That now her son was leaving,
And she was most distraught.

It was like a new bereavement –
Oh, what a rotten thing!
Just when she needed Bertram
He was summoned to the King.

The King's old henchman, Lord Lafeu,
When he'd been sent to call
Young Bertram to the King, had said,
'The King's not well at all.

'He has the strangest illness,
Its origin obscure;
His doctors all just scratch their heads –
They cannot find a cure.'

When the Countess heard these words
She clasped her hands and said,
'A friend of mine knew medicine,
But sadly he's now dead.

'His name was Gerard Narbon,
A doctor of great skill,
Who, knowing he was dying,
Requested in his will

'I care for his dear daughter;
This was his final plea.
I, of course, agreed at once,
And so she lives with me.'

Helena, the daughter,
Then began to cry.
The Countess kept on talking, though
She did so with a sigh,

'She misses her poor father
But tries so hard to please –
Such a lovely disposition,
And such worthy qualities.'

Bertram then stepped forward.
He said, 'It's time to go.
I'll miss you, mother, very much
As I am sure you know.'

The Countess said to Lord Lafeu,
'You look a decent sort,
So keep an eye on Bertram –
He's not used to life at court.'

Then Bertram said to Helena
In cool and measured way,
'Take care of my dear mother,
Look out for her, I pray.'

His manner was quite brusque and short
For little did he know
That when the lady cried, she wept
Because she loved him so.

Though mourning for her father,
Her tears fell all the more
For Bertram, who she now could see
Was walking out the door.

She'd loved him for a long, long time
But knew she held no worth
In *his* eyes, due to the fact
She was of humble birth.

He was of noble pedigree
And therefore way above
Poor Helena, who was quite sure
She'd never win his love.

For she was but a servant
And though her passion burned,
She knew it was impossible
That it would be returned.

So Bertram then departed,
Helena's love still shone.
In fact it burned more brightly
Even though the man had gone.

In silent moments on her own
The girl would slowly wander
Around the mansion, deep in thought,
And at these times she'd ponder

Upon her love for Bertram,
And the illness of the King,
Then she began to be convinced
Of a momentous thing.

'I'm sure I have the means to cure
His Majesty,' she thought,
'Contained within the remedies
That my poor father taught.

'A potion with amazing power
I know would hit the spot
And very quickly prove a cure
For what the King has got.'

So she began to think she'd go
To Paris – to the King,
But then she thought, 'There's not a chance
He'd listen to a thing,

'For I am but a lowly girl;
This hill's too steep to climb.
I'd never get to speak to him –
To try would waste my time.'

A steward heard her talking
To herself like this one day.
He crouched in hiding and he heard
All that she had to say.

He caught her at a moment
Declaring to herself
Her love for Bertram, and her fear,
That she was on the shelf.

The steward told the Countess;
He repeated every word
That through his secret watching
He had slyly overheard.

The Countess summoned Helena
When all this talk was done.
She said, 'Now tell me truthfully,
Do you adore my son?'

Embarrassed, Helena then blushed,
Her cheeks turned crimson red;
Her mind was working overtime –
'Do *you* love him?' she said.

The Countess said, 'That's no reply!
Now, tell me how you feel.'
Helena found all of this
A terrible ordeal.

'Speak up!' the Countess yelled at her.
'Don't be evasive, girl.'
Poor Helena was lost for words,
Her thoughts were in a whirl.

But finally she spoke and said,
'Yes, ma'am, I love your son,
And though I know it's wrong of me,
For me, he is the one.

'I know our love can never be,
The social gap's too wide,
So I would never let him know
How I feel deep inside.'

The Countess made no comment,
But she asked, 'And is it true
You plan to go to Paris?
And then what will you do?'

This was her aim, Helena said,
'I think that I can bring
Some succour and assistance,
And maybe cure the King.'

The Countess uttered not a word –
Approval nor of blame –
But she was thinking that the girl
Might somehow make her name.

For if she cured the sickly King
There'd simply be no end
To his relief and gratitude;
He'd always be her friend.

And so the Countess bid her go,
She wished her 'best of luck,'
Without a doubt she did admire
Her bravery and pluck.

When Helena reached Paris then
She begged Lord Lafeu's aid,
And an appointment with the King
Was very quickly made.

When asked to take the potion
The King would not concur.
He said, 'I'll not take medicine
From one the likes of her.'

And though he was still feeling
Extremely weak and low,
He said, 'You must be joking –
Whatever could she know?'

Helena stayed very calm,
She stood there quite serene;
Then quietly she told the King
Just who her dad had been.

This really made him listen,
For Narbon was *the* man.
He thought, 'If anything can cure,
I'm sure *his* potions can.'

But still he was reluctant,
So Narbon's daughter said,
'If you're no better in two days
I'll sacrifice my head.'

So finally the King agreed
But said, 'Let me be plain:
If you don't bring about a cure,
If I'm not right as rain

'Within the passing of two days,
Well then it's sad to say,
You'll lose your life immediately,
Upon that very day.

'But if it works, then as reward
For taking such a chance,
I'll give you any man you want
From all the men in France.

'And then you shall be married
To the husband of your choice.'
So spoke the sick and ailing King
In weak and trembling voice.

The trust that Helena reposed
Upon her father's skills
Was happily well-founded –
For his potions and his pills

Were just the thing – they did the trick,
The King sat up in bed.
'I feel as if I'm good as new –
Completely cured,' he said.

The King was faithful to his word;
He gathered all the court.
He said, 'Choose any man you want,
It's what your skill has bought.'

'I feel as if I'm good as new'

Then Helena looked round the room
And saw him standing there –
The man she loved, dear Bertram –
And with a silent prayer

She said, 'This is the man I want;
This is the one, my Lord.'
But sadly Bertram did not feel
Of similar accord.

He made it very clear to all.
He said, 'My gracious sir,
She is a common maiden
And I do not fancy her.

'She's servant to my mother,
She is frightfully low-born.'
Poor Helena was shocked to hear
These words of total scorn.

But noblemen do not refuse
A gift from royalty.
The King said, 'Don't you dare reject
A gift that's come from me.'

And so upon that very day
The two of them were wed.
But it was not a happy time,
For it must still be said,

That though kings issue high decrees
From on their thrones above,
The greatest monarch cannot grant
The gift of man's true love.

As soon as they were married
Bertram up and told his wife,
'I am not staying here at court,
I'm off to get a life.

'You must return to mother.'
And Helena – so good –
Just bowed her head in servitude
And meekly said she would.

When she got back, the Countess was
As nice as she could be.
She said, 'That selfish boy of mine
Will be the death of me.

'How can he send you back to me
On this your wedding day?
It really doesn't do at all –
I don't know what to say.'

But then things went from bad to worse.
A servant brought a note
From Helena's new husband,
And this is what he wrote:

'My wife, I write to tell you that
You'll not see me again.
However long you wait around,
Your wait will be in vain.

'I'll only be your husband
If you contrive to take
The ring that's on my finger –
But, my wife, make no mistake

'This ring stays on my finger,
So I think you should ensure
You don't waste time in thinking of
This husband anymore.

'But if you can obtain the ring,
Though stuck to me like glue,
Then in an instant I'll become
A loyal spouse to you.'

Helena read the hurtful words,
Her eyes glazed in a trance,
For Bertram then went on to write,
'And now I'm leaving France.'

'Oh what a naughty, selfish boy!'
The Countess cried aloud.
'You deserve a better man,
Not one that's rude and proud.'

She did the best she could to make
The poor, young girl feel better,
But her new daughter was destroyed
By this so callous letter.

Next day the young wife ran away,
Nowhere could she be found,
They couldn't find her anywhere
Though they looked all around.

And then they saw a solemn note
Inscribed in her fair hand:
'I've gone as pilgrim to the shrine
Of good Saint Jaques le Grand.

'I've gone to seek atonement
For driving him away,
I've gone to seek forgiveness,
I've gone there now to pray.

'Tell Bertram that I've run away,
And, though my love will burn,
Tell him that his detested wife
Will never now return.'

Bertram had to Florence fled,
And joined the army there,
But then he heard that his new wife
Had disappeared somewhere.

The Countess wrote to tell him
That there was no need to roam,
As Helena had gone away –
So he could now come home.

Just when he was preparing
To go and see his mum,
So Helena, all unaware,
Had made her plans to come

To Florence – as a pilgrim,
On her way to see the shrine,
And she was searching for a place
To stay awhile and dine.

She found lodgings with a widow,
A really lucky find –
For the lady gave warm welcome,
And was extremely kind.

Once Helena had settled in
She said, 'I thought you might
Be pleased to view the army,
It's really quite a sight.

'They've just come back from fighting
In the recent glorious wars,
And if you come along, you'll see
A countryman of yours.

'It is the Count of Roussillon,
He'll be there in the show.'
This was all it took to get
Poor Helena to go.

For she would now see Bertram.
They headed for the place,
And on arriving she was pleased
To see his handsome face.

The widow was excited,
She said, 'Is he not fine?
He is so rich and handsome
And he is of noble line.'

Helena, of course, agreed,
But then the widow said,
'Although he has a wife, they say
He married and then fled.

'He rushed to leave his lady,
He joined the army here,
But now he's found another girl
And holds her very dear.

'He's fallen for my daughter –
Diana is her name –
And wooing her throughout the night
Is now his devious game.

'He sits beneath her window
Almost every single night.
He sings her songs and praises her
While she keeps out of sight.

'He makes her propositions;
He does his very best
To come into her chamber while
The household's all at rest.

'Of course, my daughter won't agree.
She never would be caught
Behaving in a naughty way,
For she's a decent sort.'

What dreadful news for Helena:
That Bertram was untrue –
But with a flash of cleverness
She saw just what to do.

Apparently her Bertram
Had told the girl that day
That on the following morning
He'd be off and on his way.

He sings her songs and praises her

He'd begged Diana to allow,
(Although it wasn't right)
For him to come to her, just once,
Upon that very night.

Helena told the widow then,
'Madam, you must know
That Bertram is my husband,
And I still love him so.

'Even though he hates me
I want to do one thing,
And that is to obtain from him
A beautiful gold ring.

'Now if your daughter would agree
To meet with Bertram later,
And once she has arranged all this
Then somehow play the traitor;

'If she would let me take her place,
My husband would believe
He's meeting with your daughter,
And thus I could retrieve

'The ring he promised, if I owned,
Would then ensure I gained
My Bertram's love for evermore,'
She quietly explained.

(You will recall that Bertram
Had promised his poor wife,
'Get me to give this ring to you
And I'll be yours for life.')

The widow and her daughter said,
'We will do all we can
To help you turn your husband
Into a faithful man.'

So Helena then set about
The first part of her scheme
By sending information out
To Bertram that would seem

To indicate his wife was dead
(She did not care she lied)
For this would cause him to propose
Diana for his bride.

But it would be his Helena
Dressed up in a disguise
He wouldn't know his real wife
Stood there before his eyes.

And so young Bertram came that night
And with a lover's charm
Did everything a young man could
To totally disarm.

While Helena took pains to play
A beauty with fine grace;
And Bertram didn't recognise
His spouse's lovely face.

He asked her hand in marriage,
And still he didn't guess,
Not even when she boldly cried
A loud resounding, 'Yes!'

Finally she said to him,
'Will you give me one thing
To bind our loving union here –
Please may I have your ring?'

He gave it in a moment
And said, 'It's yours for life –
A token of the faithful love
I'll give you as my wife.'

And Helena then handed him
A lovely silver ring,
A very special gift that had
Been given by the King.

Though just before the daylight broke
Young Bertram went away,
He didn't really want to leave –
In fact, he begged to stay.

But finally he left her there.
The unsuspecting chap
Had no idea that he'd been caught
Within a honey trap.

⊰⊱

Bertram left to see his mum,
And once upon his way,
Helena to the widow said,
'Please come with me, I pray,

'To Paris – we must leave at once –
And bring Diana too,
For we must go to see the King
As there is much to do.'

But when they reached the palace,
The King had gone away.
He'd left to see the Countess
And to make a little stay.

When he beheld the Countess,
He very quickly said,
'I am extremely sorry
That poor Helena is dead.'

Everyone was quite convinced
That Helena had died.
This was, of course, as we well know,
Because the girl had lied.

Now Lord Lafeu was there; he said,
'I've thought it all along,
That Bertram caused a great offence –
He did an awful wrong.'

The King heard all he had to say,
But said, 'You know, I fear,
Yearning for those who are now dead
May keep their memory dear;

'But we should let them rest in peace
Now sadly they are dead,
And to the living show our love,'
He very calmly said.

'So I'll forgive young Bertram –
Summon him right now.'
Thus Bertram came before the King
And gave a sweeping bow.

He said, 'I'm truly sorry
For everything I've done.'
The King said he'd forgive him,
'Because you are the son

'Of my old friend, your father,
And of the Countess here,
And for the sake of Helena
Who's gone from us I fear.'

The King then gave his pardon.
He said he would restore
The young man to his favour
And call him 'friend' once more.

But almost as the words came out
His face creased in a frown:
The silver ring of Helena
He saw on looking down.

It was on Bertram's finger.
How had he got the ring?
For this had been a gift to her
From France's grateful King.

It looked distinctly fishy.
The King said, 'Tell me sir,
That silver ring is Helena's –
Did you steal it from her?'

Bertram was really flummoxed –
And then he boldly lied.
All knowledge of fair Helena
He there and then denied.

He said, 'A woman threw this from
A window, up above;
It was a silly gesture
Of hero worship love.'

But the King was well aware
That Bertram loathed his wife,
And felt that it looked likely
He had taken her poor life.

'Seize him!' the King commanded.
Bertram shook in great alarm
As a large and burly soldier
Grabbed him firmly by the arm.

But then the widow entered;
She came onto the scene.
The King asked rather angrily,
'Whatever does this mean?'

Diana then came in – and she
Addressed the crowded room.
She asked the King to, there and then,
Make Bertram be her groom.

She said that this rogue, Bertram,
Had said he'd marry her.
Bertram turning to the King
Said, 'This is untrue, sir.'

'Seize him!' the King commanded

Diana showed them all the ring –
She said, 'You gave me this,
And promised that you'd marry me
And sealed it with a kiss.'

It was the ring he'd given
To fair Helena that night,
Which she'd passed to Diana –
But now they got a fright,

Because the King said, 'Seize her!
Hold Bertram and this maid.
I think the pair are murderers –
I'm very much afraid

'That they have killed poor Helena,
And if I find it's so,
Then to the executioner
The two of them will go.'

Diana now was petrified
But then she begged the King,
'Please let my mother fetch the man
From whom we bought this ring.'

The widow went and then came back,
And to their great surprise
There stood the lovely Helena,
Alive before their eyes.

The Countess was quite overjoyed,
She cried, 'My dear, it's you.'
The King with great amazement said,
'Can all these things be true?

'Is this young Bertram's ill-used wife?'
She answered, 'To my shame,
I'm but the shadow of a spouse,
A wife in only name.'

Then, turning to her husband, she
Declared, 'I now must say
It was your wife with whom you slept
Only the other day.

'But I'm sure you will recall,
That you were of a mind
To be extremely amorous,
And also very kind.

'You gave me this love token, which
Is such a lovely thing.'
She took it from Diana then
And handed him the ring.

'You gave me this, dear Bertram,
And you'll recall you said
The day I made the bauble mine,
We'd be completely wed.

'So I command you faithfully,
Do what you said you'd do:
Become a loving husband now,
Be steady, upright, true.'

Bertram replied, 'With all my heart,
And I will prove to be
Most faithful and most loving –
Rely on it, you'll see.'

What an amazing turnaround –
The strangest ever heard!
And Bertram from that day was true
And loyal to his word.

The King said to Diana then,
'You've helped this lady so,
We'll find a worthy husband
For you too, before you go.'

What it is to be a King –
Whatever can one say?
It is a King's prerogative
To match-make in this way.

So everything was sorted out.
There's nothing more to tell;
And happily it's true to say
All's well, that ended well!